SRA Imagine It!

Lesson Assessment Book 2

Level 5

Annotated Teacher's Edition

McGraw Hill SRA

A Division of The *McGraw-Hill* Companies

SRAonline.com

 SRA

Printed in the United States of America.

Send all inquiries to this address:
SRA/McGraw-Hill
4400 Easton Commons
Columbus, OH 43219-6188

ISBN: 978-0-07-613229-4
MHID: 0-07-613229-3

2 3 4 5 6 7 8 9 MAZ 13 12 11 10 09 08

The McGraw·Hill Companies

Table of Contents

Imagine It! Lesson Assessment Books

Lesson Assessment Book 1 and *Lesson Assessment Book 2* are an integral part of a complete assessment program that aligns with the instruction in *Imagine It! Lesson Assessment Book 1* covers material from Units 1–3. *Lesson Assessment Book 2* covers material from Units 4–6. The skills featured in lesson assessments are tied to reading success and reflect both state and national standards.

Lesson Assessment Book 1 and *Lesson Assessment Book 2* offer the opportunity for summative and formative assessment. As students complete each lesson, they will be assessed on their understanding of the instructional content and the literature in each lesson. The results of the assessments will then be used to inform subsequent instruction. How students score on the assessments offers a picture of current student achievement status while also guiding you toward appropriate instructional decisions.

Each lesson assessment offers you the ability to gauge students' understanding of and growth in the following areas:

- Vocabulary
- Comprehension
- Grammar, Usage, and Mechanics
- Oral Fluency
- Writing

Lesson Assessments

The lesson assessments consist of the following:

Lesson Area	Format	Scope	Scoring
Vocabulary	Multiple Choice	Selection Vocabulary and Word Structure elements	10 points (5 questions x 2 point)
Comprehension	Multiple Choice	Comprehension Skills	5 points (5 questions x 1 point)
	Short Answer	Comprehension Skills	10 points (5 questions x 2 points)
	Linking to the Concepts (Short Answer)	General comprehension related to a selection	4 points (0-4 rubrics)
	Personal Response (Short Answer)	General comprehension related to a selection	3 points (0-3 rubrics)
	Analyzing the Selection (Extended Response)	Understanding and development of ideas about selections and the unit theme	8 points (0-8 rubrics)
Grammar, Usage, and Mechanics	Multiple Choice	Grammar, Usage, and Mechanics skills practiced in the lesson	10 points (5 questions x 2 point)
Oral Fluency	Teacher-Directed Student Performance	Oral fluency development from lesson to lesson	Accuracy Rate on 100-point scale

Students will be graded on their understanding of the vocabulary, word structure, comprehension, and grammar, usage, and mechanics skills taught in the lesson on a 50-point scale. A score of 80% (or 40 points out of 50) or higher on each lesson assessment is expected. Students may look back at the selection to answer the assessment questions. Students who consistently fall below 80% should be monitored for possible intervention. Students who are consistent low-performers in one or more aspects of the lesson assessment should be offered more practice in this lesson area during Workshop.

The Oral Fluency Assessments are scored separately. These assessments offer further data on student abilities. Student performance on oral fluency assessments is often a reliable predictor of student growth and understanding in other lesson areas. Students with consistently low accuracy rates and below-level words per minute numbers should be provided extra fluency practice during Workshop.

End of Unit Writing Prompt

Over the course of the year, students will encounter six writing prompts, two each in the narrative, expository, and persuasive genres. These prompts reflect students' prior knowledge and experience with writing to a specific genre. Each prompt consists of a writing situation, a specific audience, directions for writing, and a checklist students can reference to ensure they receive the best score possible. Rubrics for scoring student work follow each prompt in this book. These rubrics pertain to genre, writing traits, and conventions. Students will be graded on a 20-point scale based on the rubrics—four points multiplied by five key writing features.

A score of 75% (or 15 points out of 20) or higher on each writing prompt is expected. Students can respond to the prompts in their student workbooks.

Scores and Records

The opening page of each lesson assessment includes a place for students to write their names and the date, and for you to list their scores.

The Oral Fluency Assessment includes a box in which to write the accuracy rate.

The writing prompt includes a place for students to write their names and the date, and for you to list their scores.

Students' scores in the assessment can be registered in the Oral Fluency Scores, Class Assessment Record, and Student Assessment Record pages.

Lesson Assessment Sections

Students may look back at the selection to answer the assessment questions.

Vocabulary

Each vocabulary assessment is comprised of five multiple-choice questions worth two points each. Four of the questions feature selection vocabulary words from the lesson students have just completed. The remaining question in the assessment pertains to a word structure element from that lesson. The format of this question varies based on the word structure feature that is being assessed.

Comprehension: Multiple Choice

Each comprehension assessment begins with five multiple-choice questions worth one point each. The items reflect the comprehension skills students have been taught specifically in that lesson and skills students have been previously taught.

Comprehension: Short Answer

Next, students answer five short-answer questions worth two points each. These questions also reflect comprehension skills specific to the lesson and to students' prior knowledge and understanding of comprehension skills. Well-crafted and concise responses that answer the question fully should be awarded two points. Answers that partially address the question or are confusing and incomplete should be awarded a point, at your discretion. Answers that do not attempt to address the question or provide incorrect information should receive zero points.

Please note the "Possible answers below" following the directions in this Teacher's Edition. This serves as a reminder that students do not have to provide the exact answer shown, and that in some cases more than one answer is possible. For example, questions that ask for "one reason" or "one example" of something might be answered by a reason or example not specified in this Teacher's Edition.

Comprehension: Linking to the Concepts

In this section, students craft a response to a question related to the selection they have just read. These questions do not focus on a particular comprehension skill; rather, they assess general comprehension of a selection by focusing on a key element in a selection which students should be comfortable identifying and writing to or about. These questions are worth four points each. Use the following criteria to judge student responses. To fully answer the question or prompt, student answers should be approximately forty to seventy words.

Score: 4
The student understands the question and responds using information from the selection. The response is correct, reflects a thorough comprehension of the selection, and is an acceptably complete answer to the question. The organization of the response is meaningful, it is written smoothly, and sentences flow together. The response focuses on the topic. If multiple paragraphs are written, they are linked to one another with effective transitions. The response reads easily and demonstrates a sense of audience. It has correct spelling, grammar, usage, and mechanics, and it is written neatly and legibly.

Score: 3
The student understands the question and responds using information from the selection. The response may reflect comprehension of the selection and is a somewhat complete answer to the question. The organization of the response is meaningful, it is written smoothly, and sentences flow together. The response focuses on the topic. If multiple paragraphs are written, they are linked to one another with effective transitions. The response reads easily and demonstrates a sense of audience. It has occasional errors in spelling, grammar, usage, and mechanics, and it is mostly written neatly and legibly.

Score: 2
The student has partial understanding of the question. The response may reflect limited comprehension of the selection and is an incomplete answer to the question. The organization of the response is weak, it is written carelessly, and sentences are somewhat disorganized. The response includes extraneous information. If multiple paragraphs are written, they are linked to one another ineffectively. The response requires some effort to read easily and demonstrates a poor sense of audience. It has occasional errors in spelling, grammar, usage, and mechanics, and it is written somewhat neatly and legibly.

Score: 1
The student has minimal understanding of the question. The response may reflect poor comprehension of the selection and is a barely acceptable answer to the question. The organization of the response is imprecise, it is written erratically, and sentences may be disjointed. The response is poorly focused. If multiple paragraphs are written, they are linked to one another inconsistently. The response is difficult to follow and may cause the reader to struggle. It has frequent errors in spelling, grammar, usage, and mechanics, and it is written with borderline neatness and legibility.

Score: 0

The student fails to compose a response. If a response is attempted, it is inaccurate, meaningless, or irrelevant. The response may be written so poorly that it is neither legible nor understandable.

SAMPLE

The following is an example of a response that would receive a score of "3" if it were mostly written neatly and legibly. The student shows an understanding of the question and relates information pertaining to the selection. The answer is organized, and the sections of the response relate to one another. However, the lack of an example for current wind use and the errors in spelling and grammar prevent it from being an exemplary response.

Linking to the Concepts How has wind been valuable to people throughout history?
    People have used wind for a long time. The first way to use wind was probably a boat. These were made a long time ago. Windmills came next. Windmills were used to create power for businesses. They still use windmills in some places; popepl continue to use wind everyday.

Comprehension: Personal Response

In this section, students are asked to craft a personal response related to an idea or thematic issue raised by the selection they have just read. This section judges students' level of comprehension by assessing their ability to connect what they have just read to a personal level.

These questions are worth three points each. Use the following criteria to judge student responses. To fully answer the question or prompt, student answers should be approximately forty to seventy words.

Score: 3

The student understands the question and responds suitably using a personal experience, opinion, prior knowledge, or plausible conjecture. The response reflects a thorough comprehension of the selection and is an acceptably complete answer to the question. The organization of the response is meaningful, it is written smoothly, and sentences flow together. The response focuses on the topic. If multiple paragraphs are written, they are linked to one another with effective transitions. The response reads easily and demonstrates a sense of audience. It has correct spelling, grammar, usage, and mechanics, and it is written neatly and legibly.

Score: 2

The student understands the question and responds using a personal experience, opinion, prior knowledge, or plausible conjecture. The response may reflect partial comprehension of the selection and is a somewhat complete answer to the question. The organization of the response is imprecise, it is written erratically, and sentences may be somewhat disjointed. The response is not clearly focused. If multiple paragraphs are written, they are linked to one another ineffectively. The response is difficult to follow and demonstrates little awareness of the reader. It has a moderate number of errors in spelling, grammar, usage, and mechanics, and it is mostly written neatly and legibly.

Score: 1

The student has minimal understanding of the question and responds using a personal experience, opinion, prior knowledge, or plausible conjecture. The response may reflect poor comprehension of the selection and is a barely acceptable answer to the question. The organization of the response is imprecise, it is written erratically, and sentences may be disjointed. The response is poorly focused. If multiple paragraphs are written, they are linked to one another inconsistently. The response is difficult to follow and may cause the reader to struggle. It has frequent errors in spelling, grammar, usage, and

Score: 0

The student fails to compose a response. If a response is attempted, it is inaccurate, meaningless, or irrelevant. The response may be written so poorly that it is neither legible nor understandable.

The following is an example of a response that would receive a score of "2" if it were mostly written neatly and legibly. The student shows an understanding of the question and connects it to plausible, real-world situations. However, the details about the shirts and the time it took to finish the walk are unnecessary, and there are errors in grammar. These facts prevent it from being an exemplary response.

SAMPLE

Personal Response *Think about what Paul Revere did. Write about something you did that was part of a bigger event involving other people.*

> *My mother and I tried to do something important like Revere. We went for a walk to support a cure for cancer. It was a huge event. We paid money and got shirts. We wore our shirts on the walk. The walk took a long time almost an hour. Some of the people ran and we all hoped that what we did would help find a cure.*

Grammar, Usage, and Mechanics

Each grammar, usage, and mechanics assessment is comprised of five multiple-choice questions worth two points each. Each question specifically relates to the lesson material for that week. Students sometimes will be asked to identify errors or incorrect constructions, so remind students to read each question carefully.

Comprehension: Analyzing the Selection

This section of the assessment allows students to craft a longer, more detailed response to show their comprehension of what they have read. It also provides additional data on the writing skills of students as they progress through the program.

Students will sometimes be asked to respond by connecting the selection they have just read to previous selections in the unit.

These questions and prompts are worth eight points each. Use the following criteria to judge student responses. To fully answer the question or prompt, student answers should be approximately one hundred to one hundred and sixty words.

Note: You will notice that the rubrics below each have a two-point range. Use your professional judgment in awarding the higher point total in the scale to students' work.

Score: 8 or 7

The student understands the question and responds suitably using the appropriate source of information. These sources include the selection itself, other selections, personal experience, opinion, prior knowledge, or plausible conjecture. The response reflects a thorough comprehension of the selection and is an acceptably complete answer to the question. The organization of the response is meaningful, it is written smoothly, and both sentences and paragraphs flow together. Paragraphs focus on related topics and are linked to one another with effective transitions. The response reads easily and demonstrates a sense of audience. It has correct spelling, grammar, usage, and mechanics, and it is written neatly and legibly.

Score: 6 or 5

The student understands the question and responds suitably using the appropriate source of information. These sources include the selection itself, other selections, personal experience, opinion, prior knowledge, or plausible conjecture. The response may reflect comprehension of the selection or other sources and is a somewhat complete answer to the question. The organization of the response is somewhat meaningful, and both sentences and paragraphs flow together relatively smoothly. Paragraphs focus on related topics and are linked to one another with effective transitions. The response reads easily and demonstrates a sense of audience. It has occasional errors in spelling, grammar, usage, and mechanics, and it is written somewhat neatly and legibly.

Score: 4 or 3

The student has partial understanding of the question. The response may reflect limited comprehension of the selection and is an incomplete answer to the question or includes irrelevant information. The organization of the response is weak, it is written carelessly, and both sentences and paragraphs are somewhat disorganized. Paragraphs include some extraneous information and are linked to one another ineffectively. The response requires some effort to read easily and demonstrates a poor sense of audience. It has occasional errors in spelling, grammar, usage, and mechanics, and it is written somewhat neatly and legibly.

Score: 2 or 1

The student has minimal understanding of the question. The response may reflect poor comprehension of the selection and is a barely acceptable answer to the question or includes irrelevant information. The organization of the response is imprecise, it is written erratically, and sentences or paragraphs may be disjointed. Paragraphs may be poorly focused or are linked to one another inconsistently. The response is difficult to follow and may cause the reader to struggle. It has frequent errors in spelling, grammar, usage, and mechanics, and it is written with borderline neatness and legibility.

Score: 0

The student fails to compose a response. If a response is attempted, it is inaccurate, meaningless, or irrelevant. The response may be written so poorly that it is neither legible nor understandable.

The following is an example of a response that would receive a score of "4" if written somewhat neatly and legibly. The student shows a partial understanding of the question through the use of examples from the selections. The student makes occasional errors in spelling and grammar. However, the chief concern is that the theme the student identifies—how different people made the West—is not supported by the examples from the selections. This makes the response disorganized and less than convincing.

SAMPLE

Analyzing the Selection *Think about the three selections you have read in this unit. What are some common themes among them? What do these themes tell about the American West?*

One was about buffalo and how Native Americans hunted them. They used the buffalo for everything. They ate the meat and used the skin. When the buffalo were gone the people had a hard time. They probably didn't think the buffalo would ever disappear.

The story about Uncle and Wong was intresting. They were pretty smart. They found gold that other people didn't know about. They pretended to be poor so no one would take their gold.

The rodeo story was about a cowboy who was a rodeo rider. People liked to watch him because he did neat things. He traveled all over the world.

The idea that was the same in all the stories is that different people helped to make the west. These three stories were mostly about people you don't see on television or in the movies. Native Americans, Chinese people, and an African American cowboy.

Oral Fluency Assessments

Administering Oral Fluency Assessments

The Oral Fluency Assessment is an efficient means for evaluating students' ability to read. It is simple to administer and score, yet it provides extraordinarily useful quantitative and qualitative data. You will find oral fluency assessments for each lesson. The words in the selections are of sufficient variety to allow for an analysis of the decoding and vocabulary abilities of a student and to draw inferences about a student's ability to derive meaning from the text.

Make a copy of the Oral Fluency Assessment for each student you will be assessing. Have students turn to the corresponding page in their workbooks. Be sure you have a pen or pencil, a stopwatch or other timer, and extra paper to record any observations. Briefly review the text before you begin. On the Oral Fluency Scores pages, you will record the student's name, the date of the assessment, and the results of the assessment.

Have the student sit comfortably at a table with you. Seat yourself and the student so that you can mark the assessment unobtrusively without distracting the student.

Say: *Here is a selection I would like you to read aloud for me. I am going to listen to you read and take some notes. The notes I take will help me learn how well you can read. You will not be graded for this, so you should not feel nervous. Read the selection carefully and do your best. Take a few minutes now to look over the selection, and then I will tell you when to begin.*

Allow time for the student to preview the story. Be sure you have a pen or pencil.

Say: *Are you ready?* (Check to be sure the student is ready.) *You may begin now.*

Start the timer or watch as the student begins to read. You may pronounce any proper nouns with which the student is unfamiliar. Do not count these words as errors.

Note: If the student becomes frustrated or makes several consecutive errors, stop the assessment.

At the end of one minute place a bracket ( ]) at the end of the last word the student reads.

Scoring Oral Fluency Assessments

The following guidelines will help you score the assessment accurately and consistently.

- Self-correcting should not be counted as an error.
- Repeating the same mistake should be counted as only one error.
- Hesitating for more than five seconds—at which point you would have provided the word—should count as an error.
- Become familiar with the evaluating codes before administering the Oral Fluency Assessment.

Scoring Conventions

- Draw a line through any word that is misread. Count this as an error. If possible, note the type of error. (Misreading *short a* as *short e*, reading *get* as *jet*, and so on).
- Draw a bracket ( ]) at the end of the last word the student reads in one minute.
- Words the student omits should be counted as errors, even if you prompt the student.
- Indicate with a caret extra words that have been inserted. If possible, write the inserted word. Count insertions as errors.
- Draw an arrow between words that have been reversed. Count these as one error.
- Students might repeat words on occasion. Do not count this behavior as an error.

Finding the Student's Accuracy Rate

To find a student's accuracy rate, count the total number of words read in one minute. The numbers beside the passage on the teacher's page will make this an easier task. Subtract the number of errors from the total number of words read and use that figure to find the number of correct words read per minute. Then divide the correct words per minute by the total number of words read to find the accuracy rate. Record these numbers on the Reading Rate and Accuracy chart located on your Oral Fluency Assessment pages.

- Record the student's score on the Oral Fluency Scores pages and the Student Assessment Record.
- Complete the Reading Fluency scale at the bottom of your Oral Fluency Assessment page. These qualitative measures indicate your subjective judgment of how the student compares with other students who are reading at grade level.

READING RATE AND ACCURACY

Total Words Read:	147
Number of Errors:	22
Number of Correct Words Read Per Minute (WPM):	125
Accuracy Rate:	85%

(Number of Correct Words Read per Minute ÷ Total Words Read)

READING FLUENCY

	Low	Average	High
Decoding ability	○	○	●
Pace	○	●	○
Syntax	○	●	○
Self-correction	○	●	○
Intonation	○	○	●

Interpreting the Oral Fluency Assessments

First, compare the student's number of correct words per minute with the following chart. This will give you an idea of how the student compares with other students in the same grade at the same time of year. The data in this chart represents the approximate number of correct words read per minute a student should be reading in Grades 2–6. The two rows of numbers represent the 50th and 75th percentiles.

	Units 1-2	Units 3-4	Units 5-6	
Grade 2	79	100	117	75th Percentile
	51	72	89	50th Percentile
Grade 3	99	120	137	75th Percentile
	71	92	107	50th Percentile
Grade 4	119	139	152	75th Percentile
	94	112	123	50th Percentile
Grade 5	139	156	168	75th Percentile
	110	127	139	50th Percentile
Grade 6	153	167	177	75th Percentile
	127	140	150	50th Percentile

Source Adapted from Hasbrouck, J., & Tindal, G. (2005). Oral Reading Fluency: 90 Years of Measurement (Tech. Rep. No. 33). Eugene, Oregon: University of Oregon, College of Education, Behavioral Research and Teaching.

Then examine the student's accuracy rate. Reading accuracy should remain constant or gradually increase within a grade and between grades, until it stabilizes at ninety percent or higher. You may find it helpful to compare a student's accuracy rate after each administration to ensure that it remains constant or increases.

Next, examine the types of errors the student is making and consider how they represent underlying student behaviors. Here are some examples:

- Inserting extra words suggests that the student understands what is read, is constructing meaning, but is reading somewhat impulsively.

- A student who refuses to attempt to read a word is probably uncertain of his or her abilities and is unwilling to take risks.

- Misreading regular letter sounds implies that the student has not yet mastered the conventions of the sound-symbol relationship. This is in contrast with the student who misreads complex letter sounds (alternate sounds, blends, diphthongs, digraphs, and so on) but has little difficulty with regular letter sounds.

Finally, consider the error pattern. If errors are scattered randomly throughout the passage, then the error types represent skills the student has not yet developed. If errors increase in frequency from beginning to end, then fatigue or inattention likely are involved.

Other Considerations

Several strategies are available for promoting reading fluency and accuracy. These involve pairing an accomplished reader with a developing reader, small-group choral reading, and repeated readings of familiar text.

You may find it useful to establish targets for reading accuracy. These targets may include goals such as reading ten words in a row without error, increasing by increments the number of correct words a student reads in a minute, or decreasing a specific error type. Establishing such targets allows you to provide appropriate instructional support and gives students a reasonable goal.

End of Unit Writing Prompt

The writing prompt offers the opportunity for an on-demand writing performance similar to the type students will encounter in high-stakes testing. Use the rubrics that follow the prompts to judge students' work. Student writing should be included in each student's Writing Portfolio.

Teacher Records

This Teacher's Edition contains record keeping material that will help you keep track of student progress in lesson assessments.

Six Point Rubrics

Six Point Writing Rubrics for assessing student writing are included.

These can take the place of the four point rubrics if you are in a school that uses the six point rubric system.

Oral Fluency Scores

These pages allow you to note student accuracy rates throughout the year.

Class Assessment Record

These pages offer a warehouse for class scores.

The spaces following the student's name allow for the recording of student scores in each lesson assessment (out of the 50-point scale) and each writing prompt (using the four point or six point rubrics to assess).

The format of the Class Assessment Record provides an easy way to monitor student growth across the year.

Student Assessment Record

You can duplicate this page for each student and use it to track student progress.

Comprehension Observation Log

Observing students as they read anthology selections is an effective way to learn their strengths and areas of need in comprehension. Use the Comprehension Observation Log to record your observations of students. Choose a small set of students to focus on for a particular lesson. You might want to observe students more than once to get a clear idea of their comprehension of texts. Copy this page for each student or group of students you observe.

Name _____ Date _____ Score _____

The Universe

Vocabulary

Read each item. Fill in the bubble for the answer you think is correct.

1. The Greek root **scope** means

   Ⓐ to look.   Ⓒ to listen.

   Ⓑ to speak.   Ⓓ to sell.

2. To **detect** means to

   Ⓐ explode.   Ⓒ guess.

   Ⓑ prove.   Ⓓ notice.

3. New stars are the bright lights inside the **bulges** at the top of the nebula. **Bulges** are

   Ⓐ rounded parts that swell out.

   Ⓑ measurements used in space.

   Ⓒ lights seen without telescopes.

   Ⓓ dark clouds that drift apart.

4. The Milky Way Galaxy is a vast **spiral** of stars. A **spiral** is

   Ⓐ a globe that rotates.

   Ⓑ a narrow jet of clouds.

   Ⓒ a curve that keeps winding.

   Ⓓ a series of rings made of gases.

5. The universe may keep expanding, or it may eventually **collapse.** To **collapse** means to

   Ⓐ come back around.

   Ⓑ fall in on itself.

   Ⓒ stick together.

   Ⓓ rebuild itself.

The Universe (continued)

Comprehension

Read the following questions carefully. Then completely fill in the bubble of each correct answer. You may look back at the selection to find the answer to each of the questions.

1. Which of these is classified as a star?

   Ⓐ the Sun

   Ⓑ the Moon

   Ⓒ Earth

   Ⓓ the Galaxy

2. Which statement about the Moon is true?

   Ⓐ It is sometimes called Alpha Centauri.

   Ⓑ It is one of the "inner planets."

   Ⓒ It is Earth's nearest neighbor in space.

   Ⓓ It is at the center of our galaxy.

The Universe (continued)

3. Jupiter and Saturn are both examples of

Ⓐ young stars.

Ⓑ giant outer planets.

Ⓒ distant galaxies.

Ⓓ new nebula clusters.

4. What causes scientists to believe they may find other solar systems?

Ⓐ the improvement in telescope technology

Ⓑ the age of the inner and outer planets

Ⓒ the number of new planets being found

Ⓓ the gas-and-dust disks forming around young stars

5. A planetary nebula is

Ⓐ a cluster of new stars being born.

Ⓑ a new planet in the making.

Ⓒ a cloud of glowing gases around an aging star.

Ⓓ a dead star that roams throughout the galaxy.

The Universe (continued)

Read the following questions carefully. Use complete sentences to answer the questions. Possible answers below

6. Explain what a light-year is and how it is used.

   It is the distance light travels in one year. It measures distance in space.

7. How do planetary nebulas differ from one another?

   They come in many shapes, such as bright globes and space pods.

8. Why does the author use the phrase "our lonely part of space" to describe our position in the Milky Way?

   Other parts of the Milky Way are much more crowded with stars.

9. At the end of the selection, the author asks a series of questions. What do these questions suggest about humankind's knowledge about space?

   The more we learn about space, the more questions we have about it.

10. What is a black hole?

    It is a region of space with tightly packed matter and a strong gravitational pull.

UNIT 4 — Lesson 1

The Universe (continued)

Read the question below. Write complete sentences for your answer. Support your answer with information from the selection.

Linking to the Concepts How is the address at the beginning of the selection helpful as an introduction to the topic of space?

_____

_____

_____

_____

_____

Read the question below. Your answer should be based on your own experience. Write complete sentences for your answer.

Personal Response Is the topic of the universe mostly *interesting* or mostly *overwhelming* to you? Support your answer with details from the passage.

_____

_____

_____

_____

_____

The Universe (continued)

Grammar, Usage, and Mechanics

Read each question. Fill in the bubble beside the answer in each group that is correct. If none of the answers is correct, choose the last answer, "none of the above."

1. In which sentence is a demonstrative pronoun underlined?
   - Ⓐ A bag of groceries was on <u>the</u> table.
   - Ⓑ <u>This</u> box was on the porch.
   - **Ⓒ** Dad found <u>these</u> in the attic.
   - Ⓓ none of the above

2. In which sentence is a demonstrative pronoun underlined?
   - Ⓐ <u>Those</u> trees turn red in the fall.
   - Ⓑ A big fish lives in <u>that</u> pond.
   - Ⓒ When you see <u>them</u>, be sure to say hello.
   - **Ⓓ** none of the above

3. Which sentence contains a demonstrative pronoun?
   - **Ⓐ** Put that away.
   - Ⓒ She likes red socks.
   - Ⓑ Those boots are muddy.
   - Ⓓ none of the above

4. Which sentence has correct punctuation?
   - Ⓐ The next town is thir-teen miles away.
   - Ⓑ September has thirty-days.
   - Ⓒ The bus left at fourfifteen.
   - **Ⓓ** none of the above

5. Which sentence has a mistake in punctuation?
   - Ⓐ The family stayed in an old-fashioned inn.
   - **Ⓑ** The temperature dropped below thirty two-degrees
   - Ⓒ A hard-working team cleaned up the park.
   - Ⓓ none of the above

The Universe (continued)

Analyzing the Selection

Read the questions below. Write complete sentences for your answer. Support your answer with information from the selection.

How has reading this selection changed your understanding of the universe? What are some other things about the universe that you would like to learn more about?

_____

_____

_____

_____

_____

_____

_____

_____

_____

_____

_____

_____

_____

_____

The Universe (continued)

Oral Fluency Assessment

Raccoons

The raccoon is a funny looking creature that is found in	1–11
many parts of the United States. It is mostly gray with a long,	12–24
striped tail. A patch of black hair around a raccoon's eyes looks	25–36
like a bandit's mask. Because of its unusual appearance, a	37–46
raccoon is a favorite subject of cartoon artists.	47–54
Raccoons are mammals. Their young are born alive, and	55–63
they get milk from their mothers. Raccoons will eat almost	64–73
anything. Their favorite foods are fish, crayfish, frogs, and	74–82
turtles. They will catch mice and will eat insects, nuts, fruits,	83–93
and eggs. Farmers consider raccoons pests. They eat chickens'	94–102
eggs and farm crops, especially corn.	103–108
A raccoon's hands are very much like a monkey's hands.	109–118
They can hold things and can even turn a handle to open a	119–131
door. Raccoons like to pick up their food and wash it before	132–143
eating it. This is why they like to live near water, such as a river	144–158
or stream.	159–160
Raccoon babies are born blind. They will stay in the den,	161–171
usually in a hollow tree, for several weeks. When they get a	172–183
little older, the mother teaches them to hunt and to climb trees.	184–195
Raccoons look cuddly because of their soft fur. They are fierce	196–206
fighters, however, especially when they are protecting their young.	207–215

EVALUATING CODES FOR ORAL FLUENCY

sky   (/) words read incorrectly

blue
^ sky   (^) inserted word
          ( ]) after the last word

READING RATE AND ACCURACY

Total Words Read: _____

Number of Errors: _____

Number of Correct Words
Read Per Minute (WPM): _____

Accuracy Rate: _____

(Number of Correct Words Read per
Minute ÷ Total Words Read)

READING FLUENCY

	Low	Average	High
Decoding ability	○	○	○
Pace	○	○	○
Syntax	○	○	○
Self-correction	○	○	○
Intonation	○	○	○

Record student rates on the Oral Fluency Scores pages.

Name _____ Date _____ Score _____

Circles, Squares, and Daggers

Vocabulary

Read each item. Fill in the bubble for the answer you think is correct.

1. The suffix **-tion** tells you that a word is a

   Ⓐ adverb.   Ⓒ verb.

   Ⓑ noun.   Ⓓ adjective.

2. Another word for **dramatic** is

   Ⓐ exciting.   Ⓒ secret.

   Ⓑ dangerous.   Ⓓ hopeful.

3. The Mayas and the ancient Egyptians were **stargazers.** The word **stargazers** means people who

   Ⓐ tell stories about the stars.

   Ⓑ attempt to travel to the stars.

   Ⓒ look at and study the stars.

   Ⓓ create art that features stars.

4. The slabs of stone lean against a **vertical** rock face. If something is **vertical**, it is

   Ⓐ straight up and down.

   Ⓑ jagged and rough.

   Ⓒ filled with holes.

   Ⓓ flat and smooth.

5. Native Americans relied on **solar** events to help determine when to plant. The word **solar** means

   Ⓐ personal or private.   Ⓒ traditional or sacred.

   Ⓑ annual.   Ⓓ related to the sun.

Circles, Squares, and Daggers (continued)

Comprehension

Read the following questions carefully. Then completely fill in the bubble of each correct answer. You may look back at the selection to find the answer to each of the questions.

1. The Bighorn and Cahokia observatories are both
   - Ⓐ made from stones.
   - Ⓑ over one thousand years old.
   - Ⓒ circular in shape.
   - Ⓓ located in Montana.

2. Why is the sunlight at the Fajada Butte observatory called a "dagger"?
   - Ⓐ It is able to cut rock.
   - Ⓑ It is shaped like a knife.
   - Ⓒ It is painfully hot.
   - Ⓓ It is used as a weapon.

Circles, Squares, and Daggers (continued)

3. To determine how the Cahokia observatory worked, archaeologists had to

   Ⓐ interview local people.

   Ⓑ use a new calendar.

   Ⓒ do research in the summer.

   Ⓓ rebuild part of the site.

4. Which of these is an opinion, not a fact?

   Ⓐ Archaeoastronomy is a very exciting new field.

   Ⓑ Archaeoastronomy combines both archaeology and astronomy.

   Ⓒ Archaeoastronomy is the study of ancient observatories.

   Ⓓ Archaeoastronomy shows how people of the past observed the skies.

5. The Moose Mountain Medicine Wheel, Casa Grande, and Hovenweep Castle are all

   Ⓐ "sun rooms."

   Ⓑ cairns.

   Ⓒ observatories.

   Ⓓ ceremonies.

Circles, Squares, and Daggers (continued)

Read the following questions carefully. Use complete sentences to answer the questions. Possible answers below

6. What are some of the reasons Native Americans studied astronomy?

They did so to know when to plant, to prepare for winter, to move, and to hold ceremonies.

7. Other than being Anasazi structures, how are the Casa Grande and Hovenweep alike?

The sun shines into both through small holes.

8. How was the Chaco Canyon observatory discovered?

Anna Sofaer, an artist, was studying carvings in the canyon and found it.

9. In the following passage from the selection, what is opinion and what is fact? "The Anasazi . . . lived in the beautiful but dry country of northern New Mexico, Colorado, Utah, and Arizona around 900 years ago."

Calling the land "beautiful" is an opinion; everything else is a fact.

10. Why does the author say that the skies were the Native Americans' calendar?

The sky helped them keep track of or know when to do important things.

Circles, Squares, and Daggers (continued)

Read the question below. Write complete sentences for your answer. Support your answer with information from the selection.

Linking to the Concepts What was the connection between early Native American observatories and important tribal ceremonies?

_____

_____

_____

_____

_____

Read the question below. Your answer should be based on your own experience. Write complete sentences for your answer.

Personal Response Which of the observatories would you most like to visit? Support your answer with details from the selection.

_____

_____

_____

_____

_____

Circles, Squares, and Daggers (continued)

Grammar, Usage, and Mechanics

Read each question. Fill in the bubble beside the answer in each group that is correct. If none of the answers is correct, choose the last answer, "none of the above."

1. What are the <u>margins</u> of a word-processing document?

Ⓐ the space between lines

Ⓑ the page breaks

Ⓒ the left and right sides

Ⓓ none of the above

2. What are <u>tabs</u> used for most often?

Ⓐ to make words more obvious

Ⓑ to indent paragraphs

Ⓒ to change the size of print

Ⓓ none of the above

3. Where is the <u>header</u> of a document found?

Ⓐ at the top

Ⓒ at the end

Ⓑ at the bottom

Ⓓ none of the above

4. What is the <u>format</u> of a word-processing document?

Ⓐ who will read it

Ⓑ the way it looks

Ⓒ what it is about

Ⓓ none of the above

5. Which of these would usually be found in a <u>header</u>?

Ⓐ the mistakes in a document

Ⓑ the important ideas in a document

Ⓒ the page numbers in the document

Ⓓ none of the above

Circles, Squares, and Daggers (continued)

Analyzing the Selection

Read the question below. Write complete sentences for your answer. Support your answer with information from the selection.

What important things can archaeoastronomy teach us today?

_____

_____

_____

_____

_____

_____

_____

_____

_____

_____

_____

_____

_____

Circles, Squares, and Daggers (continued)

Oral Fluency Assessment

On Top of the World

Sir Edmund Hillary was born in New Zealand in 1919. No one could imagine his future. The Queen of England would someday knight him. Here is the story of how the young boy grew to be a great adventurer.	1–11 12–21 22–33 34–39
Edmund first tried mountain climbing on a school trip. He loved climbing right away. He climbed the local mountains whenever he could. In order to climb safely, a person must be strong and reliable. Edmund was both. By the time he was in his twenties, he was known for his climbing.	40–49 50–58 59–70 71–82 83–90
The young climber then decided to try some mountains in Europe. Through his adventures there, he met Sir John Hunt. Hunt was planning a trip to Mount Everest. It was the highest mountain on Earth. It had never been scaled.	91–100 101–110 111–122 123–130
Hunt invited Edmund to go along on the trip. The result was history. On May 29, 1953, Edmund and his Nepalese guide, Tenzing Norgay, were the first people to reach the top of the world's tallest mountain.	131–142 143–152 153–164 165–167
Hillary never forgot the people of Nepal who helped him. For years, he has raised money for schools and hospitals. He is now recognized for his climbing and his kindness.	168–177 178–189 190–197

EVALUATING CODES FOR ORAL FLUENCY

sky   (/) words read incorrectly

blue
^ sky   (^) inserted word
                          ( ]) after the last word

READING RATE AND ACCURACY

Total Words Read: _____

Number of Errors: _____

Number of Correct Words
Read Per Minute (WPM): _____

Accuracy Rate: _____

(Number of Correct Words Read per
Minute ÷ Total Words Read)

READING FLUENCY

	Low	Average	High
Decoding ability	○	○	○
Pace	○	○	○
Syntax	○	○	○
Self-correction	○	○	○
Intonation	○	○	○

Record student rates on the Oral Fluency Scores pages.

Name _____ **Date** _____ **Score** _____

The Mystery of Mars

Vocabulary

Read each item. Fill in the bubble for the answer you think is correct.

1. **Harsh** means about the same as
   - Ⓐ dusty.
   - Ⓑ bright.
   - Ⓒ long.
   - Ⓓ severe.

2. What is the meaning of the prefix *inter-?*
   - Ⓐ between
   - Ⓑ from
   - Ⓒ without
   - Ⓓ before

3. Scientists wondered if there might be **microscopic** life on the surface. Something **microscopic** is
   - Ⓐ very friendly.
   - Ⓑ very intelligent.
   - Ⓒ very small.
   - Ⓓ very old.

4. The dry, dusty world did not look **hospitable. Hospitable** means
   - Ⓐ healthy.
   - Ⓑ rocky.
   - Ⓒ inhabited.
   - Ⓓ welcoming.

5. The robot needed to **analyze** the dirt. If you **analyze** something, you
   - Ⓐ collect it in large numbers.
   - Ⓑ find out what it is made of.
   - Ⓒ push aside.
   - Ⓓ put it back together.

The Mystery of Mars (continued)

Comprehension

Read the following questions carefully. Then completely fill in the bubble of each correct answer. You may look back at the selection to find the answer to each of the questions.

1. Which of these is an opinion?

Ⓐ Rain never falls on Mars.

Ⓑ There are sand dunes on Mars.

Ⓒ Winters on Mars are so cold that part of the air freezes.

🄓 The pink sky on Mars is prettier than Earth's sky.

2. This selection is mostly about

Ⓐ the differences between Mars and Earth.

Ⓑ what makes Mars mysterious.

🄒 the exploration of Mars.

Ⓓ why Mars has red soil.

The Mystery of Mars (continued)

3. On Earth, carbon dioxide and oxygen are normally both

   Ⓐ forms of water.

   Ⓑ gases.

   Ⓒ types of dirt.

   Ⓓ minerals.

4. Which of these statements is true?

   Ⓐ Earth revolves around the sun and Mars does not.

   Ⓑ Mars is a planet and Earth is not.

   Ⓒ Earth has liquid water and Mars does not.

   Ⓓ Mars is a solid planet and Earth is not.

5. Scientists suspect that no organic molecules have been found on Mars because

   Ⓐ chemicals in the Martian soil destroy them.

   Ⓑ solar winds blow them away.

   Ⓒ Martian dust covers the molecules.

   Ⓓ sunlight causes the molecules to change.

The Mystery of Mars (continued)

Read the following questions carefully. Use complete sentences to answer the questions. Possible answers below

6. How is life on Earth protected from the extreme conditions in space?

<u>Life on Earth is protected by the atmosphere.</u>

7. Why did the scientists heat samples of soil from Mars?

<u>The scientists were testing to see if organic molecules were present.</u>

8. How did the *Sojourner* move around?

<u>It moved around on six rugged wheels at the end of flexible legs.</u>

9. Why was it important to guide the *Viking* and *Pathfinder* spacecrafts to gently rolling Martian plains for their landings?

<u>If the landings took place on rough terrain, the crafts would be ruined.</u>

10. What is missing from Mars that would make it habitable?

<u>Mars is missing air and water.</u>

UNIT 4 — Lesson 3

The Mystery of Mars (continued)

Read the question below. Write complete sentences for your answer. Support your answer with information from the selection.

Linking to the Concepts What might it mean if Mars was once surrounded by an atmosphere similar to Earth's atmosphere?

_____

_____

_____

_____

_____

Read the questions below. Your answer should be based on your own experience. Write complete sentences for your answer.

Personal Response What part of the selection was most impressive or amazing to you? Why?

_____

_____

_____

_____

_____

The Mystery of Mars (continued)

Grammar, Usage, and Mechanics

Read each question. Fill in the bubble beside the answer in each group that is correct. If none of the answers is correct, choose the last answer, "none of the above."

1. In which sentence is the independent clause underlined?
   Ⓐ A cat sat on the floor <u>where the sun was shining</u>.
   Ⓑ <u>A cat sat on the floor</u> where the sun was shining.
   Ⓒ A cat sat on <u>the floor where the sun</u> was shining.
   Ⓓ none of the above

2. In which sentence is the dependent clause underlined?
   Ⓐ <u>Although it is small,</u> this park has many visitors.
   Ⓑ Although it is small, <u>this park has many visitors</u>.
   Ⓒ Although <u>it is small, this park</u> has many visitors.
   Ⓓ none of the above

3. Which sentence includes a dependent clause?
   Ⓐ The phone kept ringing.   Ⓒ Something is wrong.
   Ⓑ No one answered it.   Ⓓ none of the above

4. Which answer is a complex sentence?
   Ⓐ A hawk flew across the valley.
   Ⓑ The creek was beautiful, so the hikers took a break.
   Ⓒ A coyote wandered through the forest.
   Ⓓ none of the above

5. Which answer has two independent clauses?
   Ⓐ The book was good, but the movie seemed dull.
   Ⓑ Although the town is small, it has a great museum.
   Ⓒ The beach becomes crowded on the weekend.
   Ⓓ none of the above

The Mystery of Mars (continued)

Analyzing the Selection

Read the questions below. Write complete sentences for your answer. Support your answer with information from the selections.

Based on what you have read so far in the unit, how has our understanding of the universe changed over time? Do you think that such great changes will continue in the future? Why or why not?

_____

_____

_____

_____

_____

_____

_____

_____

_____

_____

_____

_____

The Mystery of Mars (continued)

Oral Fluency Assessment

Plimoth Plantation

If you ever visit the coast of Cape Cod, you might see an	1–13
odd sight. On the shores of the Atlantic Ocean is a tiny town.	14–26
The houses there look strange. The people wear funny clothes.	27–36
If you ask the people questions, they will tell you all about	37–48
their lives. They act as if it is 1627!	49–57
No, you have not traveled into the past. This place is called	58–69
Plimoth Plantation. This is the same Plymouth where the	70–78
Pilgrims landed. Everybody has heard about the Pilgrims.	79–86
They came to America in 1620. They landed in what is now	87–98
Massachusetts. They made friends with the Native Americans	99–106
and established the tradition we now call Thanksgiving.	107–114
The Plimoth Plantation that sits on the Cape Cod shore	115–124
is a living history museum. There are no glass cases in this	125–136
museum. There are no security guards. There are no paintings.	137–146
There are no tour guides. You can touch things in this museum,	147–158
and the exhibits talk to you.	159–164
Some people think history is boring. So historians got an	165–174
idea. Forget stuffy museums, they said. We should build a	175–184
village just like the Pilgrims lived in. People can see what their	185–196
life was like.	197–199

**EVALUATING CODES
FOR ORAL FLUENCY**

sky   (/) words read incorrectly

blue
^ sky   (^) inserted word
        ( ]) after the last word

READING RATE AND ACCURACY

Total Words Read: _____

Number of Errors: _____

Number of Correct Words
Read Per Minute (WPM): _____

Accuracy Rate: _____

(Number of Correct Words Read per
Minute ÷ Total Words Read)

READING FLUENCY

	Low	Average	High
Decoding ability	○	○	○
Pace	○	○	○
Syntax	○	○	○
Self-correction	○	○	○
Intonation	○	○	○

Record student rates on the Oral Fluency Scores pages.

Name _____ Date _____ Score _____

Apollo 11: First Moon Landing

Vocabulary

Read each item. Fill in the bubble for the answer you think is correct.

1. Which word means the opposite of **bulky?**
   - Ⓐ warm
   - Ⓑ broken
   - ⬤ tiny
   - Ⓓ fast

2. **Sensations** are
   - Ⓐ challenges.
   - ⬤ feelings.
   - Ⓒ radio waves.
   - Ⓓ moon rocks.

3. When a rocket takes off, there is a great **thrust.**
   A **thrust** is a
   - Ⓐ low rumble.
   - Ⓑ bright flash.
   - Ⓒ loud sound.
   - ⬤ strong force.

4. A **hatch** is part of a ship or spacecraft. What is a **hatch?**
   - ⬤ a type of opening
   - Ⓑ a type of fin or rudder
   - Ⓒ a small engine
   - Ⓓ a landing device

5. The moon landing gave many people a sense of **awe. Awe** means
   - Ⓐ responsibility.
   - Ⓑ anger.
   - ⬤ wonder.
   - Ⓓ doubt.

Apollo 11: First Moon Landing (continued)

Comprehension

Read the following questions carefully. Then completely fill in the bubble of each correct answer. You may look back at the selection to find the answer to each of the questions.

1. Which of these is an opinion?

   Ⓐ Neil Armstrong was the mission commander.

   Ⓑ The Moon landing was the most important exploration in history.

   Ⓒ When the astronauts returned to Earth, they were greeted as heroes.

   Ⓓ Astronaut Collins inspected the lunar module for damage.

2. What is the main idea of this selection?

   Ⓐ The first Moon landing was an important and dangerous trip.

   Ⓑ Mission Control kept in almost constant contact with Apollo 11.

   Ⓒ It took several hours for the men to put on their space suits.

   Ⓓ People all over the world watched the Moon landing.

Apollo 11: First Moon Landing (continued)

3. Why were many people left speechless by the sight of a man on the Moon?

   Ⓐ They were angry it had taken so long.

   Ⓑ They were disappointed by the quality of the images.

   Ⓒ They were not sure what they were seeing.

   Ⓓ They were awed by the accomplishment.

4. Where did the *Apollo 11* land when it returned to Earth?

   Ⓐ in a large lake in Florida

   Ⓑ in the Sea of Tranquility

   Ⓒ in the Pacific Ocean

   Ⓓ in the Atlantic Ocean

5. Why did the astronauts have their shortest rest period the day before the Moon landing?

   Ⓐ They were too excited to sleep.

   Ⓑ They were on a tight schedule.

   Ⓒ They had to deal with the radio blackout.

   Ⓓ They needed to fix the hatch.

Apollo 11: First Moon Landing (continued)

**Read the following questions carefully. Use complete
sentences to answer the questions. Possible answers below**

6. What happened right after *Apollo 11* passed behind the
   dark side of the Moon?

   The astronauts lost radio contact with
   Mission Control.

7. Why did Armstrong say, "The *Eagle* has wings"?

   He said that because the *Eagle* had
   been released from the *Columbia.*

8. Why was the Sea of Tranquility chosen for the *Eagle's*
   landing site?

   It was chosen because it was a safe
   area, open and flat, on which to land.

9. Why was the astronauts' success so important?

   This was the first time human beings
   had landed on the Moon.

10. Why did Mission Control tell the astronauts, "You've got
    a bunch of guys about to turn blue"?

    The people at Mission Control had
    been holding their breath nervously.

Apollo 11: First Moon Landing (continued)

Read the question below. Write complete sentences for your answer. Support your answer with information from the selection.

Linking to the Concepts Why did Aldrin tell Congress that the footprints on the Moon belonged to the American people?

_____

_____

_____

_____

_____

Read the questions below. Your answer should be based on your own experience. Write complete sentences for your answer.

Personal Response If you could go where no human had gone before, would you? Why or why not?

_____

_____

_____

_____

_____

Apollo 11: First Moon Landing (continued)

Grammar, Usage, and Mechanics

Read each question. Fill in the bubble beside the answer in each group that is correct. If none of the answers is correct, choose the last answer, "none of the above."

1. Which of these is a sentence fragment?
   - (A) Almost no one there.
   - (C) It was snowing.
   - (B) The city expected crowds.
   - (D) none of the above

2. Which of these is a run-on sentence?
   - (A) The space shuttle normally lands in Florida.
   - (B) Weather is bad in other places.
   - (C) The shuttle must be flown back to the Space Center.
   - (D) none of the above

3. In which sentence do the subject and verb agree?
   - (A) A few geese lives there all year.
   - (B) A group of people stood under the awning.
   - (C) The chairs on the deck gets wet in a storm.
   - (D) none of the above

4. Which sentence has a mistake in subject-verb agreement?
   - (A) A box of toys were loaded into the car.
   - (B) Local families donate money to the shelter.
   - (C) The workers at the shelter care for many people.
   - (D) none of the above

5. Which sentence has correct punctuation?
   - (A) The truck didn't have enough gas for the trip.
   - (B) "We'll get some in a few minutes said the driver."
   - (C) The trucks tank hold's fifty gallons of gas.
   - (D) none of the above

Apollo 11: First Moon Landing (continued)

Analyzing the Selection

Read the questions below. Write complete sentences for your answer. Support your answer with information from the selection.

The United States has not landed a person on the Moon in many years. How important do you think it is to continue exploration using astronauts? Are the risks involved worth what is gained?

_____

_____

_____

_____

_____

_____

_____

_____

_____

_____

_____

_____

Apollo 11: First Moon Landing (continued)

Oral Fluency Assessment

Our Strange Geography

Most people think that sand dunes are only on beaches. The — 1–11
Great Sand Dunes National Monument, however, is in Colorado. — 12–20
It is at the foot of the Rocky Mountains. That is a thousand — 21–33
miles from the nearest ocean. Wind and weather have created — 34–43
great sand dunes there. The area is not far from some of the — 44–56
best skiing in the United States. — 57–62

Speaking of skiing, Taos Ski Valley is known for its steep — 63–73
slopes and perfect snow. This beautiful resort is located — 74–82
in a state we think of as being hot and dry. That state is — 83–96
New Mexico. — 97–98

Canada and Mexico share a border with the United States. — 99–108
They are our closest neighbors. The next closest is Russia. — 109–118
Parts of Russia are less than a mile from Alaska. Speaking of — 119–130
Alaska, our largest state stretches across four time zones. The — 131–140
rules have been bent a little. Just one time zone is used for the — 141–154
whole state. — 155–156

About a third of Michigan is separated from the rest of the — 157–168
state. That area is called the Upper Peninsula. The region is — 169–179
actually connected to Wisconsin. — 180–183

What strange geography do you have in your home state? — 184–193

**EVALUATING CODES
FOR ORAL FLUENCY**

sky   (/) words read incorrectly

blue
 ^ sky   (^) inserted word
       ( ]) after the last word

READING RATE AND ACCURACY

Total Words Read: _____

Number of Errors: _____

Number of Correct Words
Read Per Minute (WPM): _____

Accuracy Rate: _____

(Number of Correct Words Read per
Minute ÷ Total Words Read)

READING FLUENCY

	Low	Average	High
Decoding ability	○	○	○
Pace	○	○	○
Syntax	○	○	○
Self-correction	○	○	○
Intonation	○	○	○

Record student rates on the Oral Fluency Scores pages.

Name _____ Date _____ Score _____

Ellen Ochoa: Reaching for the Stars

Vocabulary

Read each item. Fill in the bubble for the answer you think is correct.

1. The Greek root **graph** means about the same as

Ⓐ to read.　　　　　Ⓒ to speak.

Ⓑ to run.　　　　　**Ⓓ** to write.

2. Another word for **precise** is

Ⓐ exact.　　　　　Ⓒ quick.

Ⓑ sloppy.　　　　　Ⓓ new.

3. Today Ochoa works to **advance** space exploration. In this sentence, **advance** means

Ⓐ to try to find something.

Ⓑ to finish doing something.

Ⓒ to help the progress of something.

Ⓓ to point out problems with something.

4. To carry out these important missions takes **confidence.** **Confidence** is

Ⓐ years of study.

Ⓑ faith in oneself.

Ⓒ support from others.

Ⓓ willingness to practice.

5. Ochoa waited to hear about her **application** with NASA. An **application** is a type of

Ⓐ mission.　　　　　**Ⓒ** request.

Ⓑ teacher.　　　　　Ⓓ job.

Ellen Ochoa: Reaching for the Stars (continued)

Comprehension

Read the following questions carefully. Then completely fill in the bubble of each correct answer. You may look back at the selection to find the answer to each of the questions.

1. On her first mission to space, Ochoa
   Ⓐ helped to install a truss at the ISS.
   Ⓑ gathered information about the ozone.
   Ⓒ retrieved a satellite using the robot arm.
   Ⓓ transferred supplies to the crew of the ISS.

2. When did Ochoa decide to become an astronaut?
   Ⓐ while watching the first moon landing on television
   Ⓑ when she heard about a Russian female cosmonaut
   Ⓒ after getting her Ph.D. from Stanford
   Ⓓ after moving near the Johnson Space Center

Ellen Ochoa: Reaching for the Stars (continued)

3. Based on the information in the selection, you can infer that Ochoa

   Ⓐ was a dedicated student.

   Ⓑ saw humor in everyday things.

   Ⓒ was a promising athlete.

   Ⓓ enjoyed music most of all.

4. Why did a professor discourage Ochoa from pursuing an engineering career?

   Ⓐ The professor thought that her work was below standard.

   Ⓑ The professor suspected that engineering was a dying field.

   Ⓒ The professor saw that she liked other subjects more.

   Ⓓ The professor believed that engineering was for men.

5. Which of these probably most influenced Ochoa to apply at NASA?

   Ⓐ having a mother for a strong role model

   Ⓑ knowing that other women had been hired

   Ⓒ being honored by her middle school teachers

   Ⓓ knowing the job carried a potential for danger

Ellen Ochoa: Reaching for the Stars (continued)

Read the following questions carefully. Use complete sentences to answer the questions. Possible answers below

6. List two jobs, in the order that Ochoa did them, using the "robot arm."

She put a satellite into position next to the Discovery; she retrieved a satellite.

7. How does Ochoa work "to make life better for everyone else"?

She studies the sun; she assists with space research; she is a role model.

8. What types of supplies does Ochoa transfer to the ISS?

She transports clothes, computers, cables, medicine, and equipment.

9. How is the RMS or robot arm like a real arm?

The robot arm has wrists and joints.

10. According to Ochoa, why is the ISS important?

Beneficial research happens at the ISS, and space exploration is being advanced there.

Ellen Ochoa: Reaching for the Stars (continued)

Read the question below. Write complete sentences for your answer. Support your answer with information from the selection.

Linking to the Concepts What might Ochoa's example communicate to young girls of today?

_____

_____

_____

_____

_____

Read the question below. Your answer should be based on your own experience. Write complete sentences for your answer.

Personal Response If you could have any career you wanted, what would that career be? Explain your choice.

_____

_____

_____

_____

_____

_____

Ellen Ochoa: Reaching for the Stars (continued)

Grammar, Usage, and Mechanics

Read each question. Fill in the bubble beside the answer in each group that is correct. If none of the answers is correct, choose the last answer, "none of the above."

1. Which sentence contains a demonstrative pronoun?

  (A) When will you be going to the post office?

  (B) These letters do not have stamps on them.

  (C) The delivery service left that on the porch.

  (D) none of the above

2. Which sentence has a singular demonstrative pronoun?

  (A) Please hand this to grandmother.

  (B) Those can be recycled.

  (C) Put these in a brown paper bag.

  (D) none of the above

3. Which sentence is correct?

  (A) Rake that part of the garden, she said.

  (B) "I'll get Jake's things," Dad said.

  (C) "Theyre next to the door I said."

  (D) none of the above

4. Which of these is a sentence fragment?

  (A) Jason started late.   (C) Our seats are near here.

  (B) Meet us at the game.   **(D)** none of the above

5. Which sentence is correct?

  (A) The wood for the fires are stacked beside the garage.

  (B) The fireplace is nice we use it on cold nights.

  (C) Reading in front of the fire is wonderful.

  (D) none of the above

Ellen Ochoa: Reaching for the Stars (continued)

Analyzing the Selection

Read the questions below. Write complete sentences for your answer. Support your answer with information from the selections.

What types of abilities and interests do scientists and astronauts share? How are they similar, and how are they different?

_____

_____

_____

_____

_____

_____

_____

_____

_____

_____

_____

_____

_____

_____

_____

_____

Ellen Ochoa: Reaching for the Stars (continued)

Oral Fluency Assessment

Redwood Trees

Every part of the country has a special tree that is native to	1–13
that region. On the northwest coast of the United States, the	14–24
special tree is the redwood. These tall, reddish-brown trees	25–34
grow in beautiful forests. They usually grow near the ocean.	35–44
Redwood trees need a great deal of moisture. Being near the	45–55
ocean provides them with ample exposure to rain and fog.	56–65
Redwoods grow to be very old. Some live for hundreds of	66–76
years. Scientists know the age of these trees by looking at	77–87
their growth rings. If a redwood tree is cut crossways, you can	88–99
see these rings. A ring is formed for each year of a tree's life.	100–113
Researchers study redwood tree rings to learn the age of the	114–124
tree and what the climate and environmental conditions were	125–133
like in the forest as the tree was growing.	134–142
The tallest trees on record are redwoods. For example, the	143–152
Rockefeller Tree, a redwood, is three hundred and sixty-seven	153–162
feet high. It is the tallest tree in the world. If you were to put	163–177
this tree on a football field, it would reach all the way from one	178–191
goalpost to the other.	192–195

EVALUATING CODES FOR ORAL FLUENCY

sky   (/) words read incorrectly

blue

^   sky   (^) inserted word

          ( ]) after the last word

READING RATE AND ACCURACY

Total Words Read: _____

Number of Errors: _____

Number of Correct Words Read Per Minute (WPM): _____

Accuracy Rate: _____

(Number of Correct Words Read per Minute ÷ Total Words Read)

READING FLUENCY

	Low	Average	High
Decoding ability	○	○	○
Pace	○	○	○
Syntax	○	○	○
Self-correction	○	○	○
Intonation	○	○	○

Record student rates on the Oral Fluency Scores pages.

Name _____ **Date** _____ **Score** _____

Narrative Writing

Writing Situation
A spaceship flight

Audience
Your friends and family

Directions for Writing
Imagine that it is the future. Write a story about a group of students your age traveling to a planet outside our solar system. Describe the spaceship and what the students do on the trip.

Checklist
You will earn the best score if you
- think about your ideas and plan your writing before you begin.
- get the reader's attention with an exciting first paragraph.
- have a good beginning, middle, and end to your story.
- make sure your ideas flow in a way that makes sense.
- use sensory words and figurative language so the reader can experience the story.
- tell about the characters in your story.
- provide details so the reader can understand the setting.
- relate the setting to the plot of the story.
- describe the problem and solution that are the basis of the plot of the story.
- tell events in the order they happen.

Four Point Rubrics for Narrative Writing

Genre	1 Point	2 Points	3 Points	4 Points
Narrative	Narrative has missing details or elements. Logical order and narrative structure is unclear. Plot does not include a viable problem. Character development is not apparent. Setting does not include descriptions of where and when the narrative is set.	Narrative includes plot outline and some descriptive details and elements that add excitement or color, but narrative structure is not entirely clear. Character development is minimal. Setting includes minimal descriptions of where and when the narrative is set.	Narrative includes fairly well developed plot with descriptive details and other elements such as subplots that are integrated into the resolution. Narrative structure is clear. Characters are developed, though some characters may seem superficial. Setting includes descriptions of where and when the narrative is set.	Narrative includes more complicated plotlines with varied timelines, flashbacks, or dual story lines. Narrative structure is well defined. Characters well defined throughout, with unique qualities integral to the plot. Setting includes detailed descriptions of where and when the narrative is set.
Narrative: Theme	No theme is apparent.	Superficial theme is included but not integrated.	A theme is expressed but not well developed.	The narrative fully develops a theme that expresses an underlying message beyond the narrative plot.
Writing Traits				
Audience	Displays little or no sense of audience. Does not engage audience.	Displays some sense of audience.	Writes with audience in mind throughout.	Displays a strong sense of audience. Engages audience.
Voice	The writing provides little sense of involvement or commitment. There is no evidence that the writer has chosen a suitable voice.	The writer's commitment to the topic seems inconsistent. A sense of the writer may emerge at times; however, the voice is either inappropriately personal or inappropriately impersonal.	A voice is present. The writer demonstrates commitment to the topic. In places, the writing is expressive, engaging, or sincere. Words and expressions are clear and precise.	The writer has chosen a voice appropriate for the topic, purpose, and audience. Unique style comes through. The writing is expressive, engaging, or sincere. Strong commitment to the topic.
Writing Conventions				
Conventions Overall	Numerous errors in usage, grammar, spelling, capitalization, and punctuation repeatedly distract the reader and make the text difficult to read. The reader finds it difficult to focus on the message.	The writing demonstrates limited control of standard writing conventions (punctuation, spelling, capitalization, grammar, and usage). Errors sometimes impede readability.	The writing demonstrates control of standard writing conventions (punctuation, spelling, capitalization, grammar, and usage). Minor errors, while perhaps noticeable, do not impede readability.	The writing demonstrates exceptionally strong control of standard writing conventions (punctuation, spelling, capitalization, grammar, and usage) and uses them effectively to enhance communication. Errors are so few and so minor that the reader can easily skim over them.

Name _____ Date _____ Score _____

Buffalo Hunt

Vocabulary

Read each item. Fill in the bubble for the answer you think is correct.

1. **Lurking** means about the same as
   - Ⓐ laughing.
   - Ⓑ preparing.
   - Ⓒ jumping.
   - Ⓓ hiding.

2. Which Latin root means "to speak"?
   - Ⓐ *form*
   - Ⓑ *dict*
   - Ⓒ *tact*
   - Ⓓ *script*

3. The buffalo hunters formed a grand **procession.**
   A **procession** is
   - Ⓐ a meal of great celebration.
   - Ⓑ a gathering place on the prairie.
   - Ⓒ a line of people moving forward.
   - Ⓓ a place of honor for the leaders.

4. Hunters would sometimes **stampede** the buffalo over cliffs. In this sentence, **stampede** means to
   - Ⓐ sneak up on a herd quietly.
   - Ⓑ observe a herd from a distance.
   - Ⓒ distract a herd with loud noises.
   - Ⓓ cause a herd to run wildly.

5. They **pitched** their tipis along the canyon floor. In this sentence, **pitched** means they
   - Ⓐ repaired their tipis.
   - Ⓑ set up their tipis.
   - Ⓒ connected their tipis.
   - Ⓓ left their tipis behind.

Buffalo Hunt (continued)

Comprehension

Read the following questions carefully. Then completely fill in the bubble of each correct answer. You may look back at the selection to find the answer to each of the questions.

1. Having so many buffalo legends shows that Plains Indians

Ⓐ wanted to warn others about the buffalo.

Ⓑ placed great importance on the buffalo.

Ⓒ believed the buffalo was their creation.

Ⓓ viewed the buffalo as a storyteller.

2. The Comanche and Blackfoot buffalo legends differ in

Ⓐ what the buffalo look like.

Ⓑ how important the buffalo are.

Ⓒ where the buffalo come from.

Ⓓ how the buffalo are used.

Buffalo Hunt (continued)

3. On the day of a hunt, the first thing the hunters did was

  Ⓐ send out the scouts.

  Ⓑ eat a quick meal.

  Ⓒ pack up the camp.

  Ⓓ gather for a discussion.

4. Why was it important for everyone to be quiet during a hunt?

  Ⓐ The buffalo could hear weak and far off sounds.

  Ⓑ The hunters had to concentrate on the herd.

  Ⓒ The hunt was a sacred act with rites and ceremonies.

  Ⓓ The buffalo made a special sound.

5. Much of the buffalo meat was made into jerky because it was

  Ⓐ a popular snack with traders.

  Ⓑ an easy recipe to make.

  Ⓒ a tough meat to chew.

  Ⓓ a way to preserve the meat.

Buffalo Hunt (continued)

Read the following questions carefully. Use complete sentences to answer the questions. Possible answers below

6. How did the arrival of horses change buffalo hunting?

The horses allowed Native Americans to travel long distances, chase the herds, and carry more possessions.

7. How did men's and women's responsibilities differ during a hunt?

The men did the hunting, and the women made their catch useful.

8. How was the scout's job different from the marshal's job?

Marshals picked and quieted a camp spot; scouts looked for buffalo.

9. Why are the artists' paintings of buffalo hunts helpful to us today?

They show how the buffalo were hunted and what life was like then.

10. What were some of the things that buffalo hides were useful for?

They were useful for tipi walls, clothing, shoes, and bags of all kinds.

Buffalo Hunt (continued)

Read the question below. Write complete sentences for your answer. Support your answer with information from the selection.

Linking to the Concepts How did the arrival of white settlers affect the buffalo hunt?

_____

_____

_____

_____

_____

Read the question below. Your answer should be based on your own experience. Write complete sentences for your answer.

Personal Response Is there a difference between killing buffalo for survival and killing buffalo for profit? Support your opinion with details from the selection.

_____

_____

_____

_____

_____

_____

Buffalo Hunt (continued)

Grammar, Usage, and Mechanics

Read each question. Fill in the bubble beside the answer in each group that is correct. If none of the answers is correct, choose the last answer, "none of the above."

1. Which sentence contains an appositive?

ⓐ The group took a walk through a nature preserve.

ⓑ Several birds flew by, but no one knew what they were.

🅒 The animal, a type of rabbit, hopped into the bushes.

ⓓ none of the above

2. Which sentence has a mistake in punctuation?

ⓐ The snow was great, and the resort was perfect.

ⓑ People enjoy different types of vacations.

🅒 The cruise was on a huge ship the *KIWI 5*.

ⓓ none of the above

3. Which sentence is in the past tense?

ⓐ The fish swim in a tank. 🅒 The dog chased a ball.

ⓑ A cat was chasing birds. ⓓ none of the above

4. Which sentence is in the present perfect tense?

ⓐ Rachel misplaced her backpack.

ⓑ She had carried it with her to school.

ⓒ Her friend found it behind a pile of books.

🅓 none of the above

5. Which sentence is in the future tense?

ⓐ All the players practiced hard for the game.

ⓑ The coaches make sure the players do their homework.

🅒 The team will travel to the game on a bus.

ⓓ none of the above

Buffalo Hunt (continued)

Analyzing the Selection

Read the questions below. Write complete sentences for your answer. Support your answer with information from the selection.

What would have happened if the buffalo had not disappeared? Would Native Americans still have kept the old ways?

_____

_____

_____

_____

_____

_____

_____

_____

_____

_____

_____

_____

_____

Buffalo Hunt (continued)

Oral Fluency Assessment

Candy for Your Health

If you had a sore throat many years ago, your doctor might	1–12
have given you candy. Your candy "cure" would have been a	13–23
small, yellow root. It was the root of a licorice plant.	24–34
For over three thousand years, people have known about the	35–44
benefits of licorice. Licorice is a flowering shrub that grows to	45–55
about four to five feet tall. The root of the plant is very sweet.	56–69
In fact, it is about fifty times sweeter than sugar!	70–79
To make the black, whip-like candy that we call licorice, the	80–91
roots from the plant are ground up and boiled. When the water	92–103
evaporates, a liquid called extract is left behind. This extract	104–113
can be used as a flavoring. And the flavor of licorice is used in	114–127
candy, tea, soft drinks, and even medicines.	128–134
Taste is not the only reason it is used in medicines. Licorice	135–146
has healing powers. It is known to build strength, to fight	147–157
stress, to ease pain, and even to stop coughs and sore throats.	158–169
A recent study suggests that licorice may even help stop the	170–180
growth of some cancers.	181–184
So the next time you have a sore throat, get to the root of the	185–199
matter. Do as the doctor ordered. Try some good old-fashioned	200–210
licorice!	211

**EVALUATING CODES
FOR ORAL FLUENCY**

sky   (/) words read incorrectly

blue
^ sky   (^) inserted word
           ( ]) after the last word

READING RATE AND ACCURACY

Total Words Read: _____

Number of Errors: _____

Number of Correct Words
Read Per Minute (WPM): _____

Accuracy Rate: _____

(Number of Correct Words Read per
Minute ÷ Total Words Read)

READING FLUENCY

	Low	Average	High
Decoding ability	○	○	○
Pace	○	○	○
Syntax	○	○	○
Self-correction	○	○	○
Intonation	○	○	○

Record student rates on the Oral Fluency Scores pages.

Name _____ Date _____ Score _____

The Journal of Wong Ming-Chung

Vocabulary

Read each item. Fill in the bubble for the answer you think is correct.

1. What is the meaning of the suffix **-ent?**

  Ⓐ made of   ⬤ having the quality of

  Ⓑ full of   Ⓓ without

2. If something is **raggedy,** it is

  ⬤ worn out.   Ⓒ new.

  Ⓑ old-fashioned.   Ⓓ expensive.

3. When food is **rationed,** it is

  Ⓐ cooked too much.

  ⬤ limited to small portions.

  Ⓒ carried away to be eaten later.

  Ⓓ tasteless and chewy.

4. Wong Ming-Chung and Uncle **registered** their claim. This means they

  Ⓐ kept it a secret.

  Ⓑ discovered it by accident.

  Ⓒ sold it.

  ⬤ recorded it officially.

5. Wong Ming-Chung had a **theory** about the gold. What is a **theory?**

  Ⓐ a way to find gold

  Ⓑ a legend

  ⬤ an opinion based on evidence

  Ⓓ a box in which gold could be kept

The Journal of Wong Ming-Chung (continued)

Comprehension

Read the following questions carefully. Then completely fill in the bubble of each correct answer. You may look back at the selection to find the answer to each of the questions.

1. What happens right after the rocker is built?
   - Ⓐ Wong Ming-Chung carries water in his hat.
   - **Ⓑ** Uncle digs up some soil.
   - Ⓒ Uncle gets discouraged.
   - Ⓓ Wong Ming-Chung runs his fingertips along the rocker's edge.

2. This selection is written from what point of view?
   - **Ⓐ** first-person point of view
   - Ⓑ second-person point of view
   - Ⓒ third-person point of view
   - Ⓓ Uncle's point of view

The Journal of Wong Ming-Chung (continued)

3. What happens last in the selection?

Ⓐ Wong Ming-Chung sneaks away to find Uncle.

Ⓑ Wong Ming-Chung tells Uncle his theory.

Ⓒ Wong Ming-Chung arrives in Sacramento.

Ⓓ Wong Ming-Chung has a nightmare about being chased by the mob.

4. When people ask Wong Ming-Chung and Uncle questions, they

Ⓐ introduce themselves.

Ⓑ answer proudly.

Ⓒ invent stories.

Ⓓ smile and say little.

5. What do Wong Ming-Chung and Uncle intend to send to China?

Ⓐ gold dust

Ⓑ money

Ⓒ mining supplies

Ⓓ letters of transit

The Journal of Wong Ming-Chung (continued)

Read the following questions carefully. Use complete sentences to answer the questions. Possible answers below

6. Why does the river look like a battlefield?

The banks of the river are filled with holes.

7. Why did Uncle say such hurtful things to Wong Ming-Chung?

He wants his nephew to go away with Fox where he will be safer.

8. Why do the Americans laugh at Wong Ming-Chung and Uncle when they register their claim?

They laugh because they think there is no gold left at the claim.

9. Why do Wong Ming-Chung and Uncle go from abandoned claim to abandoned claim?

They collect the gold dust that others have left behind.

10. Why do Wong Ming-Chung and Uncle make themselves look dirty and shabby on their trip to Sacramento?

They do not want anyone to suspect they have a basket of gold.

The Journal of Wong Ming-Chung (continued)

Read the question below. Write complete sentences for your answer. Support your answer with information from the selection.

Linking to the Concepts How do the actions of Wong Ming-Chung and Uncle show that they are clever?

_____

_____

_____

_____

_____

Read the prompt below. Your journal entry should be based on your own experience. Write complete sentences for your journal entry.

Personal Response Write a journal entry about something interesting that happened to you today. Try to include the same types of details that Wong Ming-Chung included in his journal.

_____

_____

_____

_____

_____

The Journal of Wong Ming-Chung (continued)

Grammar, Usage, and Mechanics

Read each question. Fill in the bubble beside the answer in each group that is correct. If none of the answers is correct, choose the last answer, "none of the above."

1. In which sentence is the underlined word used incorrectly?

Ⓐ When there is lightning, <u>it's</u> better to stay inside.

Ⓑ I need to stop at <u>your</u> house for a moment.

Ⓒ Julie wanted <u>to</u> enter the ski race.

Ⓓ none of the above

2. In which sentence is the underlined word used incorrectly?

Ⓐ <u>Sit</u> that box on the table.

Ⓑ Do you have <u>their</u> phone number?

Ⓒ Carlos is taller <u>than</u> Patricia.

Ⓓ none of the above

3. In which sentence is the underlined word used incorrectly?

Ⓐ Dan wants to <u>buy</u> a new bicycle.

Ⓑ A piece <u>of</u> paper fell to the floor.

Ⓒ Please <u>rise</u> the window a few inches.

Ⓓ none of the above

4. In which sentence is the underlined word used incorrectly?

Ⓐ A big truck <u>passed</u> by the park.

Ⓑ <u>Lie</u> the wood next to the garage door.

Ⓒ Our team should <u>have</u> won the game.

Ⓓ none of the above

5. Which of these is an exclamatory sentence?

Ⓐ That dish is hot!   Ⓒ This soup smells good.

Ⓑ Would you like to eat?   Ⓓ none of the above

The Journal of Wong Ming-Chung (continued)

Analyzing the Selection

Read the question below. Write complete sentences for your answer. Support your answer with information from the selection.

Why were success stories so important to the development of the American West? Use information from the selection, information you already know, and your opinion to write your response.

_____

_____

_____

_____

_____

_____

_____

_____

_____

_____

_____

_____

_____

_____

_____

The Journal of Wong Ming-Chung (continued)

Oral Fluency Assessment

Space Neighbors?

The next time you are outside on a clear night, look up. All	1–13
those stars up there are suns. They are a lot like our own sun.	14–27
Some are bigger than our sun, and some are smaller. A few are	28–40
very, very old.	41–43
Once in a while, astronomers find a planet near one of these	44–55
stars. So far, all of the planets have been cold and dead. But	56–68
some scientists think that maybe there is a planet with life on it.	69–81
And they want to communicate with that life.	82–89
Back in the 1950s, when your grandparents were young,	90–98
NASA started a program to find life on other planets. It was	99–110
called the Search for Extraterrestrial Intelligence (SETI).	111–117
They did not use spaceships to find new life. They did not use	118–130
transporters, jump gates, or other things you might see on	131–140
television or in the movies. They used plain old radios!	141–150
The scientists who worked at the SETI Institute thought that	151–160
any intelligent life probably knew about radio waves. Earth	161–169
sends out billions of weak radio waves every day. They come	170–180
from things like television broadcasts and satellites. Scientists	181–188
figured that other life might have things like that, too. So they	189–200
started watching space for certain types of radio waves.	201–209

**EVALUATING CODES
FOR ORAL FLUENCY**

sky   (/) words read incorrectly

blue

^ sky   (^) inserted word

          ( ]) after the last word

READING RATE AND ACCURACY

Total Words Read: _____

Number of Errors: _____

Number of Correct Words
Read Per Minute (WPM):   _____

Accuracy Rate: _____

(Number of Correct Words Read per
Minute ÷ Total Words Read)

READING FLUENCY

	Low	Average	High
Decoding ability	○	○	○
Pace	○	○	○
Syntax	○	○	○
Self-correction	○	○	○
Intonation	○	○	○

Record student rates on the Oral Fluency Scores pages.

Name _____ Date _____ Score _____

Bill Pickett: Rodeo-Ridin' Cowboy

Vocabulary

Read each item. Fill in the bubble for the answer you think is correct.

1. Which word best describes the following word relationship?

trip, expedition, voyage

Ⓐ schools

Ⓒ journeys ●

Ⓑ settlements

Ⓓ meetings

2. Another word for **trek** is

Ⓐ journey. ●

Ⓒ rope.

Ⓑ lesson.

Ⓓ wagon.

3. Bill performed his bulldogging **stunt** before a large rodeo crowd. In this sentence, **stunt** means a(n)

Ⓐ long speech.

Ⓑ act of skill or strength. ●

Ⓒ silly song.

Ⓓ dance move.

4. One of the cowboys gave the young Bill a **challenge.** A **challenge** is like a

Ⓐ chance to apologize for something.

Ⓑ new way of looking at something.

Ⓒ fight about something foolish.

Ⓓ dare to do something difficult. ●

5. Bill's father had helped others to grow **prospering** crops. **Prospering** means that the crops

Ⓐ were just sprouting.

Ⓒ grew year round.

Ⓑ did very well. ●

Ⓓ fed livestock.

Bill Pickett: Rodeo-Ridin' Cowboy (continued)

Comprehension

Read the following questions carefully. Then completely fill in the bubble of each correct answer. You may look back at the selection to find the answer to each of the questions.

1. Which statement about Pickett is an opinion?

   Ⓐ He became a rodeo performer.

   Ⓑ He grew up north of Austin, Texas.

   Ⓒ He was the second of thirteen children.

   Ⓓ He turned the 101 Ranch Wild West Show into a wonder.

2. Which statement expresses a fact?

   Ⓐ Watching the bulldog was an eye-popping sight.

   Ⓑ The songs made him more up-jumpy than ever.

   Ⓒ Pickett set out when he was no more than fifteen.

   Ⓓ Bill was the feistiest boy south of Abilene.

Bill Pickett: Rodeo-Ridin' Cowboy (continued)

3. Pickett's stunt was called "bulldoggin'" because he

   Ⓐ performed it with a bulldog.

   Ⓑ held the calf like the bulldog had done.

   Ⓒ was as stubborn as a bulldog.

   Ⓓ got down like a bulldog on all fours.

4. Saddling horses, mucking stalls, and lassoing steers are all

   Ⓐ rodeo stunts.

   Ⓑ riding tools.

   Ⓒ tall tales.

   Ⓓ cowhand jobs.

5. When Pickett was not performing, he was usually

   Ⓐ telling stories about his rodeo feats.

   Ⓑ keeping the old family ranch going.

   Ⓒ helping cowboys do their branding.

   Ⓓ teaching his children how to bulldog.

Bill Pickett: Rodeo-Ridin' Cowboy (continued)

**Read the following questions carefully. Use complete
sentences to answer the questions.** Possible answers below

6. Why did the Millers approach Pickett and offer him
a job?

They needed a rodeo star who could
attract big crowds.

7. What effect did traveling with the 101 Ranch Wild West
Show have on Pickett's career?

He went all over the world and even
performed for royalty.

8. Why did Pickett eventually give up performing with the
101 Ranch Wild West Show?

He wanted to spend time with family
and work rodeos closer to home.

9. How is being a cowhand similar to being a rodeo
performer? How is it different?

Both jobs work with cattle and horses;
however, the rodeo is a competition.

10. According to the selection, how did Pickett's bulldogging
affect today's rodeo?

His bulldogging helped establish
steer wrestling as a rodeo event.

Bill Pickett: Rodeo-Ridin' Cowboy (continued)

Read the question below. Write complete sentences for your answer. Support your answer with information from the selection.

Linking to the Concepts In what ways is Pickett a hero of the West?

_____

_____

_____

_____

_____

_____

Read the question below. Your answer should be based on your own experience. Write complete sentences for your answer.

Personal Response Have you ever done something that really impressed or surprised people? Write about what you did.

_____

_____

_____

_____

_____

Bill Pickett: Rodeo-Ridin' Cowboy (continued)

Grammar, Usage, and Mechanics

Fill in the bubble beside the answer that is correct.

1. Which sentence has correct punctuation?
   - Ⓐ The knives, forks, and, spoons are in that drawer.
   - Ⓑ The knives forks, and spoons are in that drawer.
   - Ⓒ The knives, forks, and spoons are in that drawer.
   - Ⓓ none of the above

2. Which sentence has correct capitalization?
   - Ⓐ She shouted, "Don't dive into the water!"
   - Ⓑ She shouted, "don't dive into the water!"
   - Ⓒ She Shouted, "don't dive into the water!"
   - Ⓓ none of the above

3. Which sentence has correct punctuation?
   - Ⓐ It had three parks: Rye: Penn: and Salk.
   - Ⓑ It had three parks: Rye, Penn and Salk.
   - Ⓒ It had three parks: Rye, Penn, and Salk.
   - Ⓓ none of the above

4. Which sentence has correct punctuation?
   - Ⓐ The cookout was fun; the whole family was there.
   - Ⓑ The cookout was; fun the whole family was there.
   - Ⓒ The cookout was fun the whole family; was there.
   - Ⓓ none of the above

5. Which sentence has correct punctuation?
   - Ⓐ Because it is raining the game, will be canceled.
   - Ⓑ Because it is raining, the game will be canceled.
   - Ⓒ Because, it is raining, the game will be canceled.
   - Ⓓ none of the above

Bill Pickett: Rodeo-Ridin' Cowboy (continued)

Analyzing the Selection

Read the questions below. Write complete sentences for your answer. Support your answer with information from the selections.

Think about the three selections you have read in this unit. What are some common themes among them? What do these themes tell about the American West?

_____

_____

_____

_____

_____

_____

_____

_____

_____

_____

_____

Bill Pickett: Rodeo-Ridin' Cowboy (continued)

Oral Fluency Assessment

A Canal Boat Vacation

For Bill and his friends, it was a dream come true. They	1–12
were about to begin a trip through the canals in France. They	13–24
would travel on a boat that had seven cabins. It also had three	25–37
bathrooms, a kitchen, a dining area, and a sitting room.	38–47
The students and their advisors had flown to France the	48–57
day before. Today they would board their boat. The King	58–67
School Boating Club had been planning the trip for a year.	68–78
The students and their advisors had raised all the money	79–88
themselves. So far, everything had gone perfectly. They could	89–97
not wait to get started.	98–102
The idea for the trip had come from the club's advisors,	103–113
Mr. and Mrs. Lesnik. They had taken a canal boat vacation	114–124
a few years earlier and really enjoyed it. They thought the	125–135
students would have a good time. In addition, they would learn	136–146
more about the people, geography, and culture of another	147–155
country.	156
The group included the Lesniks and ten club members. The	157–166
students knew they were lucky to be going on such a special	167–178
trip. They were excited about traveling overseas and seeing a	179–188
country from the deck of a canal boat.	189–196

**EVALUATING CODES
FOR ORAL FLUENCY**

sky   (/) words read incorrectly

blue
^   sky   (^) inserted word
         ( ]) after the last word

READING RATE AND ACCURACY

Total Words Read: _____

Number of Errors: _____

Number of Correct Words
Read Per Minute (WPM): _____

Accuracy Rate: _____

(Number of Correct Words Read per
Minute ÷ Total Words Read)

READING FLUENCY

	Low	Average	High
Decoding ability	O	O	O
Pace	O	O	O
Syntax	O	O	O
Self-correction	O	O	O
Intonation	O	O	O

Record student rates on the Oral Fluency Scores pages.

Name _____ Date _____ Score _____

Ghost Towns of the American West

Vocabulary

Read each item. Fill in the bubble for the answer you think is correct.

1. Which word fits in this base word family?

_____, **joyous, joyful, joyless**

- Ⓐ excited
- Ⓒ enjoyment
- Ⓑ happiness
- Ⓓ jolt

2. Another word for **evidence** is

- Ⓐ mistake.
- Ⓒ judgment.
- Ⓑ trial.
- Ⓓ proof.

3. Many settlers who came West **longed** for a better life. The word **longed** means

- Ⓐ wanted something very much.
- Ⓑ spent a lot of time on something.
- Ⓒ wrote stories or songs about something.
- Ⓓ wondered when something would happen.

4. Prospectors risked going into dangerous **territory.** A **territory** is

- Ⓐ a deep mine.
- Ⓒ a ghost town.
- Ⓑ a region of land.
- Ⓓ a mountain pass.

5. Even the hopes and dreams of ghost town **inhabitants** have blown away. **Inhabitants** are those who

- Ⓐ live in a certain place.
- Ⓑ helped build a new town.
- Ⓒ are constantly on the move.
- Ⓓ relatives who came before you.

Ghost Towns of the American West (continued)

Comprehension

Read the following questions carefully. Then completely fill in the bubble of each correct answer. You may look back at the selection to find the answer to each of the questions.

1. Most ghost towns started out as

Ⓐ mining camps.

Ⓑ large cities.

Ⓒ railroad stations.

Ⓓ wagon trails.

2. Which of these was the typical Western town least likely to have?

Ⓐ sidewalks made of wood

Ⓑ hitching posts for horses

Ⓒ a blacksmith shop

Ⓓ a railroad station

Ghost Towns of the American West (continued)

3. According to the author, finding ghost towns today is as difficult as

   Ⓐ the wagon ride westward.

   Ⓑ the founding of a camp.

   ● the search for gold.

   Ⓓ the stagecoach route.

4. Why are quotes used in this selection?

   Ⓐ to show how people in the towns talked

   ● to include observations from that time period

   Ⓒ to share what today's experts think

   Ⓓ to include dialogue between the characters

5. Which of these statements is a fact?

   Ⓐ An air of mystery swirls around the ghost towns of the American West.

   Ⓑ Sad and joyous events happened within the tumbledown walls and streets.

   Ⓒ The Americans have a perfect passion for railroads.

   ● The waves of western migration reached a peak between 1860 and 1880.

Ghost Towns of the American West (continued)

Read the following questions carefully. Use complete sentences to answer the questions. Possible answers below

6. What are some of the reasons people came to settle in the lonesome West?

<u>They wanted a better life, wanted to be rich, or sought adventure.</u>

7. Why did some people abandon their settlements in the West?

<u>They didn't make a fortune, the crops had failed, or they gave up.</u>

8. According to the selection, the California gold rush attracted what types of men?

<u>It attracted young, energetic, ragged but good-natured men from all over.</u>

9. What effect did the railroad have on a Western town?

<u>If it went through a town, that town grew. If not, it became a ghost town.</u>

10. What are most ghost towns like today?

<u>They are abandoned sites in the desert, mountains, or prairies.</u>

Ghost Towns of the American West (continued)

Read the question below. Write complete sentences for your answer. Support your answer with information from the selection.

Linking to the Concepts What are some possible reasons these western towns came to be known as "ghost towns"?

_____

_____

_____

_____

_____

_____

Read the question below. Your answer should be based on your own experience. Write complete sentences for your answer.

Personal Response What might future researchers say about your neighborhood?

_____

_____

_____

_____

_____

UNIT 5 Lesson 4

Ghost Towns of the American West (continued)

Grammar, Usage, and Mechanics

Read each question. Fill in the bubble beside the answer in each group that is correct. If none of the answers is correct, choose the last answer, "none of the above."

1. In which sentence is the underlined word a transition word?

    (A) I will light the candles before <u>everyone</u> arrives.

    (B) I will <u>light</u> the candles before everyone arrives.

    (C) I will light the candles <u>before</u> everyone arrives.

    (D) none of the above

2. Which underlined word is a transition word about time?

    (A) The cat hid <u>behind</u> him.   (C) A bird flew <u>above</u> me.

    (B) The lamb left <u>outside</u>.   (D) none of the above

3. Which underlined word is a transition word that compares?

    (A) Hikers <u>sometimes</u> write their names in this book.

    (B) This beach is <u>just as</u> nice as the other one.

    (C) <u>During</u> winter, people snowboard on this mountain.

    (D) none of the above

4. Which sentence contains a participial phrase?

    (A) My brother found a leather jacket.

    (B) Ms. Fuertes, our principal, is on vacation.

    (C) Carlos, saying little, left the stage.

    (D) none of the above

5. Which sentence contains a misplaced modifier?

    (A) Hiking up the trail, we saw rocks that were unusual.

    (B) Hiking up the trail, the rocks were unusual.

    (C) Hiking up the trail, we saw unusual rocks.

    (D) none of the above

Ghost Towns of the American West (continued)

Analyzing the Selection

Read the question below. Write complete sentences for your answer. Support your answer with information from the selection.

Suppose you and your friends came upon a ghost town. What would it be like, and what are some things you would do there?

_____

_____

_____

_____

_____

_____

_____

_____

_____

_____

_____

_____

_____

Ghost Towns of the American West (continued)

Oral Fluency Assessment

An Expensive Poster

"It's not just any old poster, Mom," Joe insisted.	1–9
"It's a lot of money for a poster," Joe's mom replied. She was	10–22
feeling just as upset as Joe.	23–28
They were talking about an ad Joe had seen in a magazine.	29–40
It was for a poster of the famous dinosaur battle scene painted	41–52
by Charles R. Knight. The original painting was in the New York	53–64
Museum of Natural History. Joe had never seen the original,	65–74
but there were copies of it in every one of his dinosaur books. It	75–88
was his favorite image of his favorite dinosaurs.	89–96
The problem with getting this amazing poster (which was a	97–106
massive forty inches by fifty inches on fabric) was the cost. If	107–118
it cost ten dollars or so, it would not be a problem. Joe had that	119–133
much in his savings. It was not, however, ten dollars. It was one	134–146
hundred dollars. That was a lot of money for a fifth-grader.	147–158
"But, Mom," Joe continued," it's the best picture ever. You	159–168
don't understand."	169–170
Joe's mother did not understand; he was right about that. She	171–181
could not dream why anybody would spend a hundred dollars	182–191
on a poster of dinosaurs.	192–196
She sighed, "We've gone over this a dozen times. If you really	197–208
want that poster, then you're going to have to earn the money	209–220
for it yourself."	221–223

**EVALUATING CODES
FOR ORAL FLUENCY**

sky   (/) words read incorrectly

blue
 ^ sky   (^) inserted word
            ( ]) after the last word

READING RATE AND ACCURACY

Total Words Read: _____

Number of Errors: _____

Number of Correct Words
Read Per Minute (WPM):   _____

Accuracy Rate: _____

(Number of Correct Words Read per
Minute ÷ Total Words Read)

READING FLUENCY

	Low	Average	High
Decoding ability	O	O	O
Pace	O	O	O
Syntax	O	O	O
Self-correction	O	O	O
Intonation	O	O	O

Record student rates on the Oral Fluency Scores pages.

Name _____ Date _____ Score _____

McBroom the Rainmaker

Vocabulary

Read each item. Fill in the bubble for the answer you think is correct.

1. The word **accurate** means

  Ⓐ correct.   Ⓒ friendly.

  Ⓑ quiet.   Ⓓ smart.

2. What is the Latin origin of the word *false?*

  Ⓐ *facil*   Ⓒ *falsus*

  Ⓑ *fabula*   Ⓓ *veritas*

3. As a farmer, McBroom must know how to **predict** the weather. To **predict** something means to

  Ⓐ work hard at it.   Ⓒ explain it.

  Ⓑ change it.   Ⓓ tell it beforehand.

4. McBroom began **sowing** seeds. **Sowing** means

  Ⓐ ordering seeds from a store.

  Ⓑ planting seeds in the ground.

  Ⓒ deciding which seeds to plant.

  Ⓓ loading seeds in a truck.

5. A **drought** is when

  Ⓐ there is little or no rain.

  Ⓑ it is time to plant your crops.

  Ⓒ there is a big harvest.

  Ⓓ there is too much rain.

McBroom the Rainmaker (continued)

Comprehension

Read the following questions carefully. Then completely fill in the bubble of each correct answer. You may look back at the selection to find the answer to each of the questions.

1. How do the mosquitoes save the farm from drought?

   Ⓐ They poke holes in the rain clouds.

   Ⓑ They help turn the beets into turnips.

   Ⓒ They put on a wonderful fireworks show.

   Ⓓ They cry hard enough to water the crops.

2. Why do the children have to teach the tadpoles to swim?

   Ⓐ The tadpoles are younger than the children.

   Ⓑ The tadpoles have lost their mothers.

   Ⓒ The tadpoles have never seen water.

   Ⓓ The tadpoles are about to become frogs.

McBroom the Rainmaker (continued)

3. This selection is written from what point of view?

Ⓐ first-person point of view

Ⓑ second-person point of view

Ⓒ third-person point of view

Ⓓ a mosquito's point of view

4. Crops and livestock are both

Ⓐ used for transportation.

Ⓑ raised on a farm.

Ⓒ harvested from the soil.

Ⓓ planted from seed.

5. Which of these was the first sign of drought?

Ⓐ the hens laid fried eggs

Ⓑ the cow gave powdered milk

Ⓒ the vegetable clocks started running slow

Ⓓ the mosquitoes began whining

McBroom the Rainmaker (continued)

Read the following questions carefully. Use complete sentences to answer the questions. Possible answers below

6. How were the children able to tell time using vegetables?

The vines grew an inch a second, and blossoms came out every minute.

7. Why does McBroom load up his wagons with topsoil?

McBroom wants to track down a rain cloud that would water the soil.

8. Why do McBroom and his children sleep under chicken wire?

They are protecting themselves from the giant biting mosquitoes.

9. What parts of this selection make it a tall tale?

It is make-believe and exaggerated. It explains things from nature.

10. How were radish seeds used as fireworks?

The children shot out the seeds, and they took root, swelled, and exploded.

McBroom the Rainmaker (continued)

Read the question below. Write complete sentences for your answer. Support your answer with information from the selection.

Linking to the Concepts In what ways is McBroom a creative thinker?

_____

_____

_____

_____

_____

_____

Read the question below. Your answer should be based on your own experience. Write complete sentences for your answer.

Personal Response Is a story like this mostly funny to you or mostly silly? Use details from the selection to support your opinion.

_____

_____

_____

_____

_____

McBroom the Rainmaker (continued)

Grammar, Usage, and Mechanics

Read each question. Fill in the bubble beside the answer in each group that is correct. If none of the answers is correct, choose the last answer, "none of the above."

1. Which sentence is in the future perfect tense?

Ⓐ The storm took everyone by surprise.

Ⓑ The sun will have melted the snow by tomorrow.

Ⓒ The snow is falling more heavily than before.

Ⓓ none of the above

2. Which sentence is in the past perfect tense?

Ⓐ Barb said she had climbed that mountain before.

Ⓑ A guide will lead us along the trail.

Ⓒ Bill made the arrangements months ago.

Ⓓ none of the above

3. Which sentence is correct?

Ⓐ She told us a story.

Ⓑ Its about how she gone home.

Ⓒ I forgot it's title.

Ⓓ none of the above

4. Which sentence is correct?

Ⓐ Sit the bag down.

Ⓑ Go set in the seat.

Ⓒ I want two pages.

Ⓓ none of the above

5. Which sentence has a participial phrase?

Ⓐ Racing down the field, Alice scored.

Ⓑ Libby scrubbed and painted the deck.

Ⓒ My sister, Brandy, is home.

Ⓓ none of the above

McBroom the Rainmaker (continued)

Analyzing the Selection

Read the questions below. Write complete sentences for your answer. Support your answer with information from the selections.

"McBroom the Rainmaker" is a tall tale. Many of the true stories of the American West are equally amazing. Think about the other selections you read in this unit. What parts of the unit were amazing or difficult to believe? Why?

_____

_____

_____

_____

_____

_____

_____

_____

_____

_____

_____

_____

McBroom the Rainmaker (continued)

Oral Fluency Assessment

A Great Cowboy

Everyone has enjoyed stories and movies about the Old	1–9
West. One of the best known stories is about cattle drives.	10–20
The ranchers in Texas had to move their cattle a long way to	21–33
market or to the railroads. A group of cowboys made sure the	34–45
cows traveled together. They also kept the cows safe.	46–54
Many of the early cowboys who drove the cattle were	55–64
African American. One cowboy, Nate Love, lived all the	65–73
adventures of the Old West. Later, he wrote a book about it.	74–85
Nate Love was born to a slave family. When he was fifteen,	86–97
he ran away and got a job as a cowpuncher on a cattle drive.	98–111
He made many trips from the ranches to the markets. In his	112–123
book, he told of fighting off wild animals, terrible weather, and	124–134
the other challenges of the Old West. The work was hard and	135–146
dirty, but Nate enjoyed it.	147–151
Adventurers such as Nate Love supplied food to the rest of	152–162
the country with their cattle drives. They also helped settle	163–172
the West. And, especially in the case of this cowboy, they left	173–184
behind a history of life on the range.	185–192

EVALUATING CODES FOR ORAL FLUENCY

sky   (/) words read incorrectly

blue
 ^ sky   (^) inserted word
           ( ]) after the last word

READING RATE AND ACCURACY

Total Words Read: _____

Number of Errors: _____

Number of Correct Words
Read Per Minute (WPM): _____

Accuracy Rate: _____

(Number of Correct Words Read per
Minute ÷ Total Words Read)

READING FLUENCY

	Low	Average	High
Decoding ability	○	○	○
Pace	○	○	○
Syntax	○	○	○
Self-correction	○	○	○
Intonation	○	○	○

Record student rates on the Oral Fluency Scores pages.

Name _____ **Date** _____ **Score** _____

Expository Writing

Writing Situation
An event that took place in the American West

Audience
Students your age from a different country

Directions for Writing
Describe an event or character from the American West. Write the description for a person your age from another country who does not know much about the American West. Include enough details so the reader will be able to visualize the event or person.

Checklist
You will earn the best score if you
- think about the event and plan your writing before you begin.
- remember that the reader will not know much about the American West.
- use sensory words and figurative language so the reader can experience the person or event.
- provide details so the reader can understand the setting.
- write complete sentences and avoid fragments or run-ons.
- write more sentences and longer sentences when you revise.
- use subjects, verbs, and modifiers correctly.
- have a good beginning, middle, and end to your story.
- avoid words and phrases that are often overused.
- read your writing after you finish and check for mistakes.

UNIT 4 — Four Point Rubrics for Expository Writing

Genre	1 Point	2 Points	3 Points	4 Points
Expository	Composition has no introduction or clear topic. It offers a group of loosely related facts or a series of poorly written steps. No conclusion is included.	Composition is clearly organized around main points with supportive facts or assertions. Composition has no clear introduction, but its topic is identifiable. However, it includes many facts unrelated to the topic, or it describes things in a disorganized way. No conclusion is included.	Main points and supportive details can be identified, but they are not clearly marked. Composition has an introduction and offers facts about the topic. Some facts may be irrelevant, or some ideas may be vague or out of order. The report is fairly well organized but doesn't have a strong conclusion.	Traces and constructs a line of argument, identifying part-to-whole relations. Main points are supported with logical and appropriate evidence. Composition begins with an introduction and offers relevant facts about the topic or describes the topic appropriately. The report is organized using cause/effect, comparison/contrast, or another pattern. It ends with a strong conclusion.

Writing Traits

	1 Point	2 Points	3 Points	4 Points
Focus	Topic is unclear or wanders and must be inferred. Extraneous material may be present.	Topic/position/direction is unclear and must be inferred.	Topic/position is stated and direction/purpose is previewed and maintained. Mainly stays on topic.	Topic/position is clearly stated, previewed, and maintained throughout the paper. Topics and details are tied together with a central theme or purpose that is maintained /threaded throughout the paper.
Ideas/Content	Superficial and/or minimal content is included.	Main ideas are understandable, although they may be overly broad or simplistic, and the results may not be effective. Supporting detail is limited, insubstantial, overly general or off topic.	The writing is clear and focused. The reader can easily understand the main ideas. Support is present, although it may be limited or rather general.	Writing is exceptionally clear, focused, and interesting. Main ideas stand out and are developed by strong support and rich details.
Elaboration (supporting details and examples that develop the main idea)	States ideas or points with minimal detail to support them.	Includes sketchy, redundant, or general details; some may be irrelevant. Support for key ideas is very uneven.	Includes mix of general statements and specific details/examples. Support is mostly relevant but may be uneven and lack depth in places.	Includes specific details and supporting examples for each key point/idea. May use compare/contrast to support.

Writing Conventions

	1 Point	2 Points	3 Points	4 Points
Conventions Overall	Numerous errors in usage, grammar, spelling, capitalization, and punctuation repeatedly distract the reader and make the text difficult to read. The reader finds it difficult to focus on the message.	The writing demonstrates limited control of standard writing conventions (punctuation, spelling, capitalization, grammar, and usage). Errors sometimes impede readability.	The writing demonstrates control of standard writing conventions (punctuation, spelling, capitalization, grammar, and usage). Minor errors, while perhaps noticeable, do not impede readability.	The writing demonstrates exceptionally strong control of standard writing conventions (punctuation, spelling, capitalization, grammar, and usage) and uses them effectively to enhance communication. Errors are so few and so minor that the reader can easily skim over them.

Name _____ Date _____ Score _____

Founders of the Children's Rain Forest

Vocabulary

Read each item. Fill in the bubble for the answer you think is correct.

1. What is the meaning of the Greek root **bio?**

  Ⓐ sun   Ⓒ land

  Ⓑ water   ⬤Ⓓ life

2. A **macaw** is a type of

  Ⓐ bear.   Ⓒ fish.

  ⬤Ⓑ parrot.   Ⓓ forest.

3. The children asked for **donations** for the rain forest. **Donations** are

  ⬤Ⓐ gifts or contributions.   Ⓒ trees to plant.

  Ⓑ animals.   Ⓓ protective laws.

4. Rain forests are usually found in the **tropics.** What are **tropics?**

  Ⓐ areas near the poles

  Ⓑ land with lots of farms

  ⬤Ⓒ areas near the equator

  Ⓓ low mountain ranges

5. Many **species** live in the rain forest. **Species** are

  Ⓐ native people.

  ⬤Ⓑ groups of related plants or animals.

  Ⓒ monkeys with short tails.

  Ⓓ colorful birds.

Founders of the Children's Rain Forest (continued)

Comprehension

Read the following questions carefully. Then completely fill in the bubble of each correct answer. You may look back at the selection to find the answer to each of the questions.

1. The author wrote this selection to
   Ⓐ convince people to visit a rain forest.
   🅑 tell about an important project students did.
   Ⓒ show why Sweden is such a nice place.
   Ⓓ explain how to buy a rain forest.

2. The students wanted Mrs. Kern to
   🅐 find a rain forest they could buy.
   Ⓑ teach them how to earn money.
   Ⓒ go on a field trip to the jungle.
   Ⓓ tell them about other places they could save.

Founders of the Children's Rain Forest (continued)

3. The children were not afraid to ask for money because

   Ⓐ they knew they would not be refused.

   Ⓑ they already had more than they needed.

   Ⓒ they knew what they wanted to do with the money was important.

   Ⓓ they had asked Kinsman for permission to raise money.

4. The amount of money Fagervik students raised

   Ⓐ was not enough to buy any rain forest.

   Ⓑ was much more than they first expected.

   Ⓒ was only enough to have a party.

   Ⓓ was the same as Mrs. Kern gave them.

5. What did the tape recorder play during the slide show?

   Ⓐ people asking for help

   Ⓑ songs about nature

   Ⓒ children's voices

   Ⓓ sounds from a rain forest

Founders of the Children's Rain Forest (continued)

Read the following questions carefully. Use complete sentences to answer the questions. Possible answers below

6. What made Mrs. Kern's students interested in the rain forest?

   <u>Mrs. Kern told them that the rain forests were being destroyed.</u>

7. Why did Mrs. Kern expect Sharon Kinsman to laugh at her?

   <u>She thought Kinsman would laugh at the students' impossible mission.</u>

8. How did the students feel after Kinsman's slide show?

   <u>The show made them even more concerned about the rain forests.</u>

9. Why did the students keep raising money after their first big event?

   <u>They realized they needed to buy even more rain forest.</u>

10. What is the cause of Mrs. Kern's optimism at the end of the selection?

    <u>Her students' hard work and outlook give her hope for the rain forest.</u>

Founders of the Children's Rain Forest (continued)

Read the question below. Write complete sentences for your answer. Support your answer with information from the selection.

Linking to the Concepts Why is Mrs. Kern's rule about there being no bad ideas so important?

_____

_____

_____

_____

_____

_____

Read the question below. Your answer should be based on your own experience. Write complete sentences for your answer.

Personal Response How can you be responsible every day for Earth and its environment?

_____

_____

_____

_____

_____

_____

Founders of the Children's Rain Forest (continued)

Grammar, Usage, and Mechanics

Read each question. Fill in the bubble beside the answer in each group that is correct. If none of the answers is correct, choose the last answer, "none of the above."

1. In which sentence is a noun underlined?

   Ⓐ The <u>icy</u> road made driving dangerous.

   Ⓑ The icy road made driving <u>dangerous</u>.

   Ⓒ The icy road <u>made</u> driving dangerous.

   ● Ⓓ none of the above

2. In which sentence is a proper noun underlined?

   Ⓐ The <u>airport</u> was crowded with European travelers.

   ● Ⓑ The family took a winter vacation in <u>Florida</u>.

   Ⓒ <u>Everyone</u> was excited to get to the Grand Canyon.

   Ⓓ none of the above

3. In which sentence is an action verb underlined?

   ● Ⓐ The fish <u>swam</u>.   Ⓒ The pond <u>seems</u> cold.

   Ⓑ A tall bird <u>had</u> landed.   Ⓓ none of the above

4. In which sentence is a helping verb underlined?

   Ⓐ The old bridge <u>looks</u> like it is all right.

   Ⓑ A truck <u>damaged</u> the old bridge.

   ● Ⓒ A new bridge <u>will</u> be built next year.

   Ⓓ none of the above

5. In which sentence is the complete predicate underlined?

   Ⓐ Our big dog sleeps on the couch <u>in the living room</u>.

   Ⓑ <u>Our big dog</u> sleeps on the couch in the living room.

   ● Ⓒ Our big dog <u>sleeps on the couch in the living room</u>.

   Ⓓ none of the above

Founders of the Children's Rain Forest (continued)

Analyzing the Selection

Read the questions below. Write complete sentences for your response. Support your answer with information from the selection.

What do you think was the most surprising part of the selection? Why was it surprising to you?

_____

_____

_____

_____

_____

_____

_____

_____

_____

_____

_____

_____

_____

_____

Founders of the Children's Rain Forest (continued)

Oral Fluency Assessment

Going West

A fire crackled cheerfully in the kitchen fireplace as Nathan,	1–10
Ishmael, Rachel, Mother, and Father sat down for dinner.	11–19
Father seemed excited as he ladled stew into each bowl.	20–29
When everyone was served, he cleared his throat. "Your	30–38
mother and I have some news. We are thinking about joining	39–49
the wagon train going West."	50–54
Wide-eyed, Nathan and Isaac turned to one another and	55–64
started whooping with excitement. Rachel, the youngest,	65–71
was quiet. She was too young to understand what a trip like	72–83
this meant.	84–85
"We could finally have some land of our own," said Mother.	86–96
Ishmael stood up. "When do we start packing?" he asked.	97–106
"Sit down, young man," Father chuckled. "If we go, we'll	107–116
need to pack very thoughtfully, keeping in mind we can only	117–127
bring the bare essentials. We'd need a rifle so we could hunt for	128–140
food and an axe to cut wood and clear land. Mother would need	141–153
to bring a couple of pots and pans to use for cooking and her	154–167
spinning wheel to make fabric for clothing."	168–174
They could only bring what fit in their wagon, which would	175–185
be pulled by a pair of oxen. "The lighter you travel, the easier	186–198
it is," Father said. Jackson, the family dog, would probably go	199–209
along. Jackson would assist with the hunting, and he could help	210–220
protect the family during dangerous encounters.	221–226

**EVALUATING CODES
FOR ORAL FLUENCY**

sky   (/) words read incorrectly

blue
 ^   sky   (^) inserted word
              ( ]) after the last word

READING RATE AND ACCURACY

Total Words Read: _____

Number of Errors: _____

Number of Correct Words
Read Per Minute (WPM):   _____

Accuracy Rate: _____

(Number of Correct Words Read per
Minute ÷ Total Words Read)

READING FLUENCY

	Low	Average	High
Decoding ability	○	○	○
Pace	○	○	○
Syntax	○	○	○
Self-correction	○	○	○
Intonation	○	○	○

Record student rates on the Oral Fluency Scores pages.

Name _____ Date _____ Score _____

Jason and the Golden Fleece

Vocabulary

Read each item. Fill in the bubble for the answer you think is correct.

1. If something is **glistening,** it is

Ⓐ dusty. Ⓒ costly.

Ⓑ dull. 🅓 shiny.

2. What is the meaning of the Greek root **naut?**

🅐 sailor Ⓒ night

Ⓑ foot Ⓓ plant

3. The monster had no **pity** for Jason. What is **pity?**

Ⓐ money and gifts

Ⓑ extra time and attention

🅒 feelings of sorrow or sympathy

Ⓓ advice or knowledge

4. The birds that swooped through the windows were **hideous. Hideous** means

Ⓐ well-trained.

🅑 very ugly.

Ⓒ very ill.

Ⓓ large.

5. The Clashing Cliffs were two rock walls on either side of a **strait.** In this sentence, a **strait** is

Ⓐ a winding mountain path.

Ⓑ a carved figurehead on a ship.

Ⓒ a gate or entrance to a garden.

🅓 a narrow passageway of water.

Jason and the Golden Fleece (continued)

Comprehension

Read the following questions carefully. Then completely fill in the bubble of each correct answer. You may look back at the selection to find the answer to each of the questions.

1. Why does King Pelias give Jason a challenge?

   Ⓐ He wants to train Jason to be king.

   Ⓑ He hopes to be rid of Jason.

   Ⓒ He thinks Jason has become too proud.

   Ⓓ He is tired of being king.

2. Why does Jason visit King Phineas?

   Ⓐ He needs to know where to find the fleece.

   Ⓑ He is told that the king owns the fleece.

   Ⓒ He needs help gathering an army.

   Ⓓ He hopes to borrow a ship from the king.

Jason and the Golden Fleece (continued)

3. How are the gulls different from the harpies?

   Ⓐ They are birds.

   Ⓑ They move in flocks.

   Ⓒ They provide help.

   Ⓓ They fly above the sea.

4. Which of these is a clue that the author provides to let the reader know the island king is up to no good?

   Ⓐ The king lives in the land of Colchis.

   Ⓑ The king curls his lip before he speaks.

   Ⓒ The king tells Jason he can have the fleece.

   Ⓓ The king has deep purple pockets.

5. Medea's potion puts Pelias to sleep

   Ⓐ forever.

   Ⓑ for three days.

   Ⓒ for three months.

   Ⓓ for three years.

Jason and the Golden Fleece (continued)

Read the following questions carefully. Use complete sentences to answer the questions. Possible answers below

6. Why does Jason bring the fleece home with him?

   Pelias will return the crown to Aeson if Jason returns with the fleece.

7. Why does Aeson at first refuse the crown of Thebes?

   He is too tired and wants his son, Jason, to be king in his place.

8. What causes Aeson to be king once again?

   Medea gives him a potion that makes him feel like a young man.

9. What happens to Pelias at the end of this myth?

   Medea's potion makes Pelias go to sleep and never wake up.

10. What parts of this selection help classify it as a myth?

   It has a hero who goes on a quest, there is a dragon, and it's make-believe.

Jason and the Golden Fleece (continued)

Read the question below. Write complete sentences for your answer. Support your answer with information from the selection.

Linking to the Concepts In what ways does Jason show himself to be a hero?

_____

_____

_____

_____

_____

_____

Read the question below. Your answer should be based on your own experience. Write complete sentences for your answer.

Personal Response How does it feel when someone helps you to succeed? Write about a time someone helped you succeed.

_____

_____

_____

_____

_____

Jason and the Golden Fleece (continued)

Grammar, Usage, and Mechanics

Read each item. Fill in the bubble for the answer you think is correct. If none of the answers is correct, choose the last answer, "none of the above."

1. Which sentence has a possessive noun?

Ⓐ Get ready or you will miss the bus.

Ⓑ The clock runs a little fast.

Ⓒ We will buy the farmer's corn.

Ⓓ none of the above

2. Which sentence has a correct plural form?

Ⓐ The two riveres join at this spot.

Ⓑ The children are climbing the branches of the tree.

Ⓒ Empty boxs were piled beside the door.

Ⓓ none of the above

3. Where could you find biographies of famous writers?

Ⓐ Online dictionary

Ⓑ Online encyclopedia

Ⓒ Web site for office supply store

Ⓓ none of the above

4. Which of these words is a pronoun?

Ⓐ catch   Ⓒ heavy

Ⓑ table   **Ⓓ** none of the above

5. Which sentence contains an object pronoun?

Ⓐ They went to practice a little while ago.

Ⓑ Call when you are ready to leave.

Ⓒ Mom waited for us after soccer practice.

Ⓓ none of the above

Jason and the Golden Fleece (continued)

Analyzing the Selection

Read the question below. Write complete sentences for your answer. Support your answer with information from the selection.

Why do you think Jason was willing to go through so much to get the Golden Fleece? Use information from the selection and your opinion to answer the question.

_____

_____

_____

_____

_____

_____

_____

_____

_____

_____

_____

_____

_____

_____

_____

Jason and the Golden Fleece (continued)

Oral Fluency Assessment

From the Country to the City

Alexander always enjoyed the outdoors. He had grown up on
a farm so he was used to being outside all the time. He helped
with all the chores around the farm and he spent his days
cleaning out the barn, feeding the chickens and cutting wood
for the fireplace. It did not seem like work; it was just what he
did. When Alexander's family moved from the country to a big
city, he really missed those days of being on the farm.

In the city, he did not have animals to care for. There were
no wild animals that came to visit. In the country, all sorts
of animals would stroll by the farm. He would see raccoons,
rabbits, deer, and even a fox every now and then.

There was only one place nearby, on the outskirts of the
city, where animals might show up. That was a park that
was linked to open-space land the city owned. No houses or
businesses could be built on the space, and some children
said they had seen wild animals there. The open-space land
looked like a small forest and stretched for miles. Alexander
loved spending time there, and he and his friends enjoyed
hiking there.

1–10
11–24
25–36
37–46
47–60
61–71
72–82
83–95
96–107
108–118
119–128
129–139
140–150
151–162
163–172
173–183
184–193
194–203
204–205

**EVALUATING CODES
FOR ORAL FLUENCY**

sky   (/) words read incorrectly

blue
  ^   sky   (^) inserted word
            ( ]) after the last word

READING RATE AND ACCURACY

Total Words Read: _____

Number of Errors: _____

Number of Correct Words
Read Per Minute (WPM):   _____

Accuracy Rate: _____

(Number of Correct Words Read per
Minute ÷ Total Words Read)

READING FLUENCY

	Low	Average	High
Decoding ability	O	O	O
Pace	O	O	O
Syntax	O	O	O
Self-correction	O	O	O
Intonation	O	O	O

Record student rates on the Oral Fluency Scores pages.

Name _____ Date _____ Score _____

The Quest for Healing

Vocabulary

Read each item. Fill in the bubble for the answer you think is correct.

1. Another word for **task** is

    Ⓐ path.   ● job.

    Ⓑ wood.   Ⓓ tool.

2. Which word fits in this base word family?
_____, **kindly, kindness, kindliest**

    Ⓐ nice   ● unkind

    Ⓑ king   Ⓓ caring

3. On the third day, Nekumonta was **exhausted** and nearly gave up. **Exhausted** means

    Ⓐ frustrated.   Ⓒ confident.

    ● extremely tired.   Ⓓ out of food and ideas.

4. The animals of the forest showed **loyalty** to Nekumonta. **Loyalty** is

    Ⓐ bitterness and anger.

    Ⓑ mistrust and suspicion.

    Ⓒ surprise and wonder.

    ● support and affection.

5. After speaking with Nekumonta, the bear **lumbered** away. **Lumbered** means that the bear moved

    Ⓐ in a secret and sneaky way.

    Ⓑ with quiet and careful steps.

    ● in a slow and heavy way.

    Ⓓ with confidence and speed.

The Quest for Healing (continued)

Comprehension

Read the following questions carefully. Then completely fill in the bubble of each correct answer. You may look back at the selection to find the answer to each of the questions.

1. The saying "her days . . . were numbered" means that Shanewis
   - (A) was still a young woman.
   - (B) waited eagerly for spring.
   - (C) was almost ready to die.
   - (D) knew winter had arrived.

2. Why does Shanewis ask Nekumonta to take her outside?
   - (A) The weather has turned beautiful.
   - (B) The spirits of her ancestors are calling.
   - (C) The villagers are having a gathering.
   - (D) The disease is beginning to lift.

The Quest for Healing (continued)

3. Nekumonta leaves his wife in order to

Ⓐ avoid getting sick.

Ⓑ go and get her family.

Ⓒ collect some fire wood.

Ⓓ find some healing herbs.

4. Right after Nekumonta asks the bear for help, he

Ⓐ talks to a rabbit.

Ⓑ visits with a doe.

Ⓒ hears a sparkling chorus.

Ⓓ calls to the villagers.

5. The bear most likely leaves Nekumonta unharmed because he

Ⓐ knows that Nekumonta is good.

Ⓑ can tell that Nekumonta is becoming sick.

Ⓒ suspects that the great Manitou is watching.

Ⓓ knows that Shanewis is waiting for him.

The Quest for Healing (continued)

Read the following questions carefully. Use complete sentences to answer the questions. Possible answers below

6. Why does the Manitou decide to help the animals and Nekumonta?

   The Manitou is pleased by how the animals supported a human.

7. How does the Manitou show Nekumonta where to look?

   He sends a dream of a waterfall and a chorus of the Healing Waters.

8. How does bathing in the Healing Waters change Nekumonta?

   After he bathes, he has strength and all his tiredness is gone.

9. What do the villagers think of the Healing Waters?

   They are thankful for them because the plague has been defeated.

10. What are two details that help to classify this as a make-believe story?

   There are animals that talk, and it has a happily-ever-after ending.

The Quest for Healing (continued)

Read the question below. Write complete sentences for your answer. Support your answer with information from the selection.

Linking to the Concepts How is the kindness Nekumonta shows to nature repaid?

_____

_____

_____

_____

_____

Read the question below. Your answer should be based on your own experience. Write complete sentences for your answer.

Personal Response What are some ways that you can show respect for plants and animals where you live?

_____

_____

_____

_____

_____

The Quest for Healing (continued)

Grammar, Usage, and Mechanics

Read each question. Fill in the bubble beside the answer in each group that is correct. If none of the answers is correct, choose the last answer, "none of the above."

1. In which sentence is a preposition underlined?

Ⓐ The skiers <u>waited</u> for the chairlift to the top.

Ⓑ The skiers waited <u>for</u> the chairlift to the top.

Ⓒ The <u>skiers</u> waited for the chairlift to the top.

Ⓓ none of the above

2. In which sentence is a prepositional phrase underlined?

Ⓐ Shore birds walked <u>along the beach</u>.

Ⓑ <u>Waves rolled</u> in one after another.

Ⓒ At the far end of the beach were <u>some large sand dunes</u>.

Ⓓ none of the above

3. What should you do to a document you need to work on later?

Ⓐ delete it

Ⓒ highlight it

Ⓑ close it without saving

Ⓓ none of the above

4. In which sentence is the adjective used correctly?

Ⓐ This story is more funnier than the last one you told.

Ⓑ This story is funnier than the last one you told.

Ⓒ This story is more funner than the last one you told.

Ⓓ none of the above

5. Which sentence is correct?

Ⓐ The Most recenter game was the team's best.

Ⓑ the more recenter game was the Teams Best.

Ⓒ The most recent game was the team's best.

Ⓓ none of the above

The Quest for Healing (continued)

Analyzing the Selections

Read the questions below. Write complete sentences for your answer. Support your answer with information from the selections.

Think about the three selections you have read in this unit. In each selection, people did remarkable things for a good reason. How were these people and their actions alike? How were they different?

_____

_____

_____

_____

_____

_____

_____

_____

_____

_____

_____

_____

The Quest for Healing (continued)

Oral Fluency Assessment

The Steel Drum

Drums have often been made out of everyday things, like	1–10
trash can lids and empty barrels. One day, someone tried	11–20
hammering out the end of a steel barrel. The sound he or she	21–33
created was different. It was not quite right. Someone else tried	34–44
shaping the barrel end the other way. It made a kind of bowl.	45–57
Once people heard the beautiful sound this drum made, they	58–67
knew that a new type of drum had been born.	68–77
Steel drums were invented on the island of Trinidad. The	78–87
most expert steel drummers still live in that area. However, the	88–98
steel drum is now played around the world. Steel drum music is	99–110
often heard in parts of the United States, particularly in those	111–121
areas where people from the Caribbean have come to live.	122–131
The sound of the steel drum is so wonderful that one drum	132–143
is sometimes not enough. In many bands, several steel drums	144–153
usually play together. Some large steel drum bands have as	154–163
many as a hundred members. Each person plays a couple	164–173
of drums.	174–175
There are many famous steel drum bands that perform and	176–185
make recordings. These bands also compete in large annual	186–194
contests. The bands practice together for many months. They	195–203
hope to win a prize and a chance to become famous.	204–214

**EVALUATING CODES
FOR ORAL FLUENCY**

sky   (/) words read incorrectly

blue
^   sky   (^) inserted word
             ( ]) after the last word

READING RATE AND ACCURACY

Total Words Read: _____

Number of Errors: _____

Number of Correct Words
Read Per Minute (WPM): _____

Accuracy Rate: _____

(Number of Correct Words Read per
Minute ÷ Total Words Read)

READING FLUENCY

	Low	Average	High
Decoding ability	O	O	O
Pace	O	O	O
Syntax	O	O	O
Self-correction	O	O	O
Intonation	O	O	O

Record student rates on the Oral Fluency Scores pages.

Name _____ Date _____ Score _____

The White Spider's Gift

Vocabulary

Read each item. Fill in the bubble for the answer you think is correct.

1. If something is **rare,** it is

Ⓐ tiny.

Ⓒ old.

Ⓑ beautiful.

Ⓓ unusual.

2. Which prefix means "before"?

Ⓐ *pre-*

Ⓒ *mid-*

Ⓑ *re-*

Ⓓ *dis-*

3. The chieftain says that Piki is good and **noble.** In this sentence, **noble** means that Piki

Ⓐ is a performer.

Ⓒ has an inner greatness.

Ⓑ fights like a warrior.

Ⓓ has great wealth.

4. The old woman says that the older you get, the more **burdened** with care you become. If you are **burdened,** you

Ⓐ are forgetful.

Ⓑ are weighed down with a heavy load.

Ⓒ enjoy remembering the past.

Ⓓ want to solve problems by yourself.

5. At the beginning of the selection, Spider is **pleading** with everyone she meets. **Pleading** means

Ⓐ saying kind things to others.

Ⓑ asking lots of different questions.

Ⓒ chatting cheerfully about things.

Ⓓ begging for something sincerely.

The White Spider's Gift (continued)

Comprehension

Read the following questions carefully. Then completely fill in the bubble of each correct answer. You may look back at the selection to find the answer to each of the questions.

1. In this selection, some words are inside parentheses ( ). The words inside the parentheses are meant to show

Ⓐ what the director should do

Ⓑ how the actors should act.

Ⓒ what the actors should say.

Ⓓ how the stage should look.

2. Who is the last person to refuse to help Spider in scene 1?

Ⓐ a boy hunting for tea leaves

Ⓑ a girl looking for flowers

Ⓒ a woman gathering twigs

Ⓓ a boy filling a jar with water

The White Spider's Gift (continued)

3. Which of these is a hint about something that will happen later in the play?

   Ⓐ You are a good, strong young Guarani.

   Ⓑ A selfless heart is the strongest of all.

   Ⓒ Will you please place me back in my web so that I may rest?

   Ⓓ Someday I shall help you as you have helped me this day.

4. The Chieftain begins the competition by asking the boys

   Ⓐ to run a foot race.

   Ⓑ to shoot at a feather.

   Ⓒ to wrestle one another.

   Ⓓ to find the most beautiful gift.

5. Piki feels hopeless about winning because he

   Ⓐ loses all of the sports contests.

   Ⓑ is poor and cannot afford a nice gift.

   Ⓒ believes Kuma deserves to win.

   Ⓓ thinks the princess will hate his gift.

The White Spider's Gift (continued)

Read the following questions carefully. Use complete sentences to answer the questions. Possible answers below

6. In scene 1, what do Piki's actions suggest about him?

   They suggest that he is kind, caring, and takes pleasure in helping others.

7. What is Spider's gift?

   It is a lace mantle, or bridal veil, spun by Spider for Piki to give to Tukira.

8. How can you tell that Spider works all night on the gift?

   It has moon dust and flowers and stars and is intricate and full of designs.

9. How is Kuma different from Piki?

   Kuma is sneaky and dishonest, and he brags a lot; Piki is kind and helpful.

10. Based on the tests that the Chieftain gives the boys, what kind of husband does he want for his daughter?

    He wants him to be fast, strong, honest, and good with a bow and arrow.

The White Spider's Gift (continued)

Read the question below. Write complete sentences for your answer. Support your answer with information from the selection.

Linking to the Concepts How does this selection support the saying, "One good deed deserves another"?

_____

_____

_____

_____

_____

Read the question below. Your answer should be based on your own experience. Write complete sentences for your answer.

Personal Response Do you think the Chieftain is a wise man? Explain your answer fully.

_____

_____

_____

_____

_____

The White Spider's Gift (continued)

Grammar, Usage, and Mechanics

Read each question. Fill in the bubble beside the answer in each group that is correct. If none of the answers is correct, choose the last answer, "none of the above."

1. In which sentence is the independent clause underlined?

(A) The doctor told Nina <u>when she could play again</u>.

(B) <u>The doctor told Nina</u> when she could play again.

(C) The doctor told <u>Nina when she could</u> play again.

(D) none of the above

2. In which sentence is the dependent clause underlined?

(A) Dad stopped the car <u>when he heard a funny noise</u>.

(B) <u>Dad stopped the car</u> when he heard a funny noise.

(C) Dad <u>stopped the car when</u> he heard a funny noise.

(D) none of the above

3. In which sentence do the subject and verb agree?

(A) A range of mountains stand in the distance.

(B) The explorers packs carefully for the trip.

(C) Each of the explorers has a special talent.

(D) none of the above

4. In which sentence do the subject and verb agree?

(A) The bus routes is easy. (C) A group were waiting.

(B) Each have a shelter. (D) none of the above

5. Which sentence has correct punctuation?

(A) "We will open in an hour, said" the manager.

(B) "We will open in an hour," said the manager.

(C) "We will open in an hour, said the manager."

(D) none of the above

The White Spider's Gift (continued)

Analyzing the Selection

Read the question below. Write complete sentences for your answer. Support your answer with information from the selection.

Many folktales have as their theme repaying a kindness or debt. Why do you think this theme is so important to people around the world? Use information from the selection, information you know already, and your opinion to answer the question.

_____

_____

_____

_____

_____

_____

_____

_____

_____

_____

_____

_____

The White Spider's Gift (continued)

Oral Fluency Assessment

The Anasazi Tribe

Can you imagine living under the side of a cliff in a huge	1–13
apartment made out of stone and mud? An ancient tribe called	14–24
the Anasazi used to live in such places. You can even visit these	25–37
wonderful sites today. You can see how they lived.	38–46
The Anasazi lived in the Four Corners area of the Southwest.	47–57
This area includes Utah, Colorado, New Mexico, and Arizona.	58–66
The tribe lived a long time ago, from about A.D. 200 to A.D.	67–79
1300. We know when and where they lived from the ruins they	80–91
left behind.	92–93
The Anasazi made their houses with walls of stone. This	94–103
helped their homes stand up to storms and harsh winter snows.	104–114
The homes were built under a cliff which gave them added	115–125
protection. Some buildings were as high as four stories.	126–134
Within these structures were many rooms. Some had more	135–143
than two hundred rooms. They housed some four hundred	144–152
people. At the time of the Anasazi, tens of thousands of these	153–164
dwellings existed. They dotted the land for miles and miles.	165–174
Mesa Verde in the southwestern part of Colorado was the	175–184
largest of these communities. The cliff dwellings there have	185–193
given us the best picture of how this tribe lived.	194–203

**EVALUATING CODES
FOR ORAL FLUENCY**

sky   (/) words read incorrectly

blue
 ^   sky   (^) inserted word
                ( ]) after the last word

READING RATE AND ACCURACY

Total Words Read: _____

Number of Errors: _____

Number of Correct Words
Read Per Minute (WPM): _____

Accuracy Rate: _____

(Number of Correct Words Read per
Minute ÷ Total Words Read)

READING FLUENCY

	Low	Average	High
Decoding ability	○	○	○
Pace	○	○	○
Syntax	○	○	○
Self-correction	○	○	○
Intonation	○	○	○

Record student rates on the Oral Fluency Scores pages.

Name _____ Date _____ Score _____

The Story of Annie Sullivan

Vocabulary

Read each item. Fill in the bubble for the answer you think is correct.

1. Which Latin root means "to see"?

(A) *pod* (C) *void*

(B) *spect* (D) *terr*

2. Another word for **imitating** is

(A) copying. (C) chatting.

(B) teasing. (D) asking.

3. After not getting her way, Helen sat upstairs **sulking. Sulking** means that Helen was

(A) playing with toys.

(B) nibbling on the cake.

(C) pouting and acting angry.

(D) stomping and banging on things.

4. The Kellers were **disturbed** by the scene at the breakfast table. **Disturbed** means that they were

(A) pleased. (C) unimpressed.

(B) amused. (D) upset.

5. Annie **insistently** put the spoon in Helen's hand. If you do something **insistently,** you do it

(A) while talking at the same time.

(B) in a strong or firm manner.

(C) with a puzzled look on your face.

(D) in front of other people.

The Story of Annie Sullivan (continued)

Comprehension

Read the following questions carefully. Then completely fill in the bubble of each correct answer. You may look back at the selection to find the answer to each of the questions.

1. There is enough information in the selection to suggest that Sullivan

   Ⓐ finds Helen to be a shy student.

   Ⓑ was both a teacher and a trained nurse.

   Ⓒ grew up near the Keller home.

   Ⓓ had worked with blind people before.

2. When Sullivan arrives, it seems as if Helen's family has been

   Ⓐ letting Helen do as she pleases.

   Ⓑ looking for a new job for Helen.

   Ⓒ trying to teach Helen to talk.

   Ⓓ giving Helen too many sweets.

The Story of Annie Sullivan (continued)

3. According to Sullivan, what two things does Helen need to learn?

Ⓐ please and thank-you

Ⓑ obedience and love

Ⓒ letters and words

Ⓓ reading and arithmetic

4. Why does Sullivan ask if there is a place where she and Helen can be by themselves?

Ⓐ The Keller household is too noisy.

Ⓑ The Kellers live in a one-room house.

Ⓒ The Kellers keep getting involved.

Ⓓ The Keller children only want to play.

5. Helen realized that words actually stood for things when Sullivan

Ⓐ let her eat some cake.

Ⓑ taught her the difference between *mug* and *milk*.

Ⓒ spelled W-A-T-E-R in her hand.

Ⓓ showed her how to identify living creatures.

The Story of Annie Sullivan (continued)

Read the following questions carefully. Use complete sentences to answer the questions. Possible answers below

6. What kind of a teacher does Sullivan have to be in order to succeed with Helen?

   She has to be strict, firm, patient, creative, and determined.

7. When Sullivan first saw Helen, how did Helen look?

   She was pretty, but she was dirty. No one seemed to care how she looked.

8. How does Sullivan change Helen's life?

   She teaches her to identify things in her environment with words.

9. When Helen gives Sullivan a hug "of her own accord," how does Sullivan feel?

   She feels great joy, as if her heart would burst.

10. Why is Helen so wild and rude at the beginning of the selection?

    She has no words for things, and she is scared by the new person.

The Story of Annie Sullivan (continued)

Read the question below. Write complete sentences for your answer. Support your answer with information from the selection.

Linking to the Concepts How did the Keller family change because of Sullivan?

_____

_____

_____

_____

_____

_____

Read the question below. Your answer should be based on your own experience. Write complete sentences for your answer.

Personal Response What makes a great teacher? Use details from the selection and from your own experience to support your opinion.

_____

_____

_____

_____

_____

The Story of Annie Sullivan (continued)

Grammar, Usage, and Mechanics

Read each question. Fill in the bubble beside the answer in each group that is correct. If none of the answers is correct, choose the last answer, "none of the above."

1. In which sentence is the verb in the past tense?

   Ⓐ The mayor and town council meet once a month.

   Ⓑ The town bought an old farm just across the river.

   Ⓒ The old farm will become an agricultural museum.

   Ⓓ none of the above

2. In which sentence is the verb in the past perfect tense?

   Ⓐ The geese will start arriving soon.

   Ⓑ They spent the summer in Canada.

   Ⓒ Each fall, they fly thousands of miles.

   Ⓓ none of the above

3. In which sentence is the verb in the future tense?

   Ⓐ Robins build a nest.   Ⓒ The tree will have fruit.

   Ⓑ Blossoms appeared.   Ⓓ none of the above

4. Which sentence has correct punctuation?

   Ⓐ The cave was huge; it went miles into the mountain.

   Ⓑ The cave was; huge it went miles into the mountain.

   Ⓒ The cave was huge, it went miles, into the mountain.

   Ⓓ none of the above

5. Which sentence has correct punctuation?

   Ⓐ We went to three countries France Austria and Italy.

   Ⓑ We went to three countries: France, Austria, and Italy.

   Ⓒ We went to three countries, France: Austria: and Italy.

   Ⓓ none of the above

The Story of Annie Sullivan (continued)

Analyzing the Selection

Read the question below. Write complete sentences for your answer. Support your answer with information from the selections.

In the selections "Founders of the Children's Rain Forest" and "The Story of Annie Sullivan," teachers changed their students and the world forever. Why were the changes so important to the students and the world?

_____

_____

_____

_____

_____

_____

_____

_____

_____

_____

_____

_____

_____

The Story of Annie Sullivan (continued)

Oral Fluency Assessment

Homes in America

Historic American homes come in many shapes and styles. In	1–10
America's Southwest, many homes are built from adobe bricks.	11–19
These are a combination of mud and straw. Adobe homes save	20–30
energy. Heat from sunshine is stored in the walls in the winter.	31–42
Those same walls keep the inside cool in summer. Since they	43–53
look like earth, adobe houses blend in well with what is around	54–65
them.	66
Wooden houses are found in many places. The first wooden	67–76
houses were log cabins. Today's wooden buildings have what is	77–86
called a "frame." Pieces of lumber are used to create a frame.	87–98
Other materials are nailed on the frame to create the walls.	99–109
Most houses made of wood are coated with one or more colors	110–121
of paint. The paint is for protection and decoration. They must	122–132
be repainted once in a while. This is something of a bother.	133–144
However, it allows people to change the look of their house.	145–155
In some areas of North America, settlers built their homes	156–165
out of stone. This stone was either slab stone from a quarry	166–177
or river stone held together with mortar. Stone houses are the	178–188
color of the local stone, which is usually grayish. These houses	189–199
are rustic and natural looking.	200–204

EVALUATING CODES FOR ORAL FLUENCY

sky   (/) words read incorrectly

blue
^ sky   (^) inserted word
         ( ]) after the last word

READING RATE AND ACCURACY

Total Words Read: _____

Number of Errors: _____

Number of Correct Words
Read Per Minute (WPM): _____

Accuracy Rate: _____

(Number of Correct Words Read per
Minute ÷ Total Words Read)

READING FLUENCY

	Low	Average	High
Decoding ability	○	○	○
Pace	○	○	○
Syntax	○	○	○
Self-correction	○	○	○
Intonation	○	○	○

Record student rates on the Oral Fluency Scores pages.

Name _____ **Date** _____ **Score** _____

Persuasive Writing

Writing Situation
A cause that is important to you

Audience
Other students your age and their families

Directions for Writing
Think of something that is important to you. It can be something global, such as saving the rain forest, or something local, such as supporting an animal shelter. Explain what the cause is, and write about why it should be important to other people so they will support it as well.

Checklist
You will earn the best score if you
- think about your cause and why it is important to you.
- plan your writing before you begin.
- have a beginning paragraph that gets the attention of readers.
- state the cause clearly in the first paragraph.
- include facts or examples that show the cause to be important.
- state the cause several times in your writing.
- make clear what you expect the reader to do.
- show that you care about the cause.
- write in a way that is interesting to your readers.
- write complete sentences and avoid fragments or run-ons.

Four Point Rubrics for Persuasive Writing

Genre	1 Point	2 Points	3 Points	4 Points
Persuasive	Position is absent or confusing. Insufficient writing to show that criteria are met.	Position is vague or lacks clarity. Unrelated ideas or multiple positions are included.	An opening statement identifies position. Writing may develop few or more points than delineated in opening. Focus may be too broad.	Sets scope and purpose of paper in introduction. Maintains position throughout. Supports arguments. Includes effective closing.
Writing Traits				
Audience	Displays little or no sense of audience. Does not engage audience.	Displays some sense of audience.	Writes with audience in mind throughout.	Displays a strong sense of audience. Engages audience.
Focus	Topic is unclear or wanders and must be inferred. Extraneous material may be present.	Topic/position/direction is unclear and must be inferred.	Topic/position is stated and direction/purpose is previewed and maintained. Mainly stays on topic.	Topic/position is clearly stated, previewed, and maintained throughout the paper. Topics and details are tied together with a central theme or purpose that is maintained /threaded throughout the paper.
Organization	The writing lacks coherence; organization seems haphazard and disjointed. Plan is not evident. Facts are presented randomly. No transitions are included. Beginning is weak and ending is abrupt. There is no awareness of paragraph structure or organization.	An attempt has been made to organize the writing; however, the overall structure is inconsistent or skeletal. Plan is evident but loosely structured or writer overuses a particular pattern. Writing may be a listing of facts/ideas with a weak beginning or conclusion. Transitions are awkward or nonexistent. Includes beginning use of paragraphs.	Organization is clear and coherent. Order and structure are present, but may seem formulaic. Plan is evident. Reasons for order of key concepts may be unclear. Beginning or conclusion is included but may lack impact. Transitions are present. Paragraph use is appropriate.	The organization enhances the central idea and its development. The order and structure are compelling and move the reader through the text easily. Plan is evident. Key concepts are logically sequenced. Beginning grabs attention. Conclusion adds impact. Uses a variety of transitions that enhance meaning. Uses paragraphs appropriately.
Writing Conventions				
Conventions Overall	Numerous errors in usage, grammar, spelling, capitalization, and punctuation repeatedly distract the reader and make the text difficult to read. The reader finds it difficult to focus on the message.	The writing demonstrates limited control of standard writing conventions (punctuation, spelling, capitalization, grammar, and usage). Errors sometimes impede readability.	The writing demonstrates control of standard writing conventions (punctuation, spelling, capitalization, grammar, and usage). Minor errors, while perhaps noticeable, do not impede readability.	The writing demonstrates exceptionally strong control of standard writing conventions (punctuation, spelling, capitalization, grammar, and usage) and uses them effectively to enhance communication. Errors are so few and so minor that the reader can easily skim over them.

Six Point Rubrics

Use the following rubrics to assess student writing.

6 Points

The writing is focused, purposeful, and reflects insight into the writing situation. The paper conveys a sense of completeness and wholeness with adherence to the main idea, and its organizational pattern provides for a logical progression of ideas. The support is substantial, specific, relevant, concrete, and/or illustrative. The paper demonstrates a commitment to and an involvement with the subject, clarity in presentation of ideas, and may use creative writing strategies appropriate to the purpose of the paper. The writing demonstrates a mature command of language (word choice) with freshness of expression. Sentence structure is varied, and sentences are complete except when fragments are used purposefully. Few, if any, convention errors occur in mechanics, usage, and punctuation.

5 Points

The writing focuses on the topic, and its organizational pattern provides for a progression of ideas, although some lapses may occur. The paper conveys a sense of completeness or wholeness. The support is ample. The writing demonstrates a mature command of language, including precise word choice. There is variation in sentence structure, and, with rare exceptions, sentences are complete except when fragments are used purposefully. The paper generally follows the conventions of mechanics, usage, and spelling.

4 Points

The writing is generally focused on the topic but may include extraneous or loosely related material. An organizational pattern is apparent, although some lapses may occur. The paper exhibits some sense of completeness or wholeness. The support, including word choice, is adequate, although development may be uneven. There is little variation in sentence structure, and most sentences are complete. The paper generally follows the conventions of mechanics, usage, and spelling.

3 Points

The writing is generally focused on the topic but may include extraneous or loosely related material. An organizational pattern has been attempted, but the paper may lack a sense of completeness or wholeness. Some support is included, but development is erratic. Word choice is adequate but may be limited, predictable, or occasionally vague. There is little, if any, variation in sentence structure. Knowledge of the conventions of mechanics and usage is usually demonstrated, and commonly used words are usually spelled correctly.

2 Points

The writing is related to the topic but includes extraneous or loosely related material. Little evidence of an organizational pattern may be demonstrated, and the paper may lack a sense of completeness or wholeness. Development of support is inadequate or illogical. Word choice is limited, inappropriate, or vague. There is little, if any, variation in sentence structure, and gross errors in sentence structure may occur. Errors in basic conventions of mechanics and usage may occur, and commonly used words may be misspelled.

1 Point

The writing may only minimally address the topic. The paper is fragmentary or an incoherent listing of related ideas or sentences or both. Little, if any, development of support or an organizational pattern or both is apparent. Limited or inappropriate word choice may obscure meaning. Gross errors in sentence structure and usage may impede communication. Frequent and blatant errors may occur in the basic conventions of mechanics and usage, and commonly used words may be misspelled.

Unscorable

The paper is unscorable because

- the response is not related to what the prompt requested the student to do.
- the response is simply a rewording of the prompt
- the response is a copy of a published work.
- the student refused to write.
- the response is illegible.

- the response is incomprehensible (words are arrange in such a way that no meaning is conveyed).
- the response contains an insufficient amount of writing to determine if the student was attempting to address the prompt.

Oral Fluency Scores

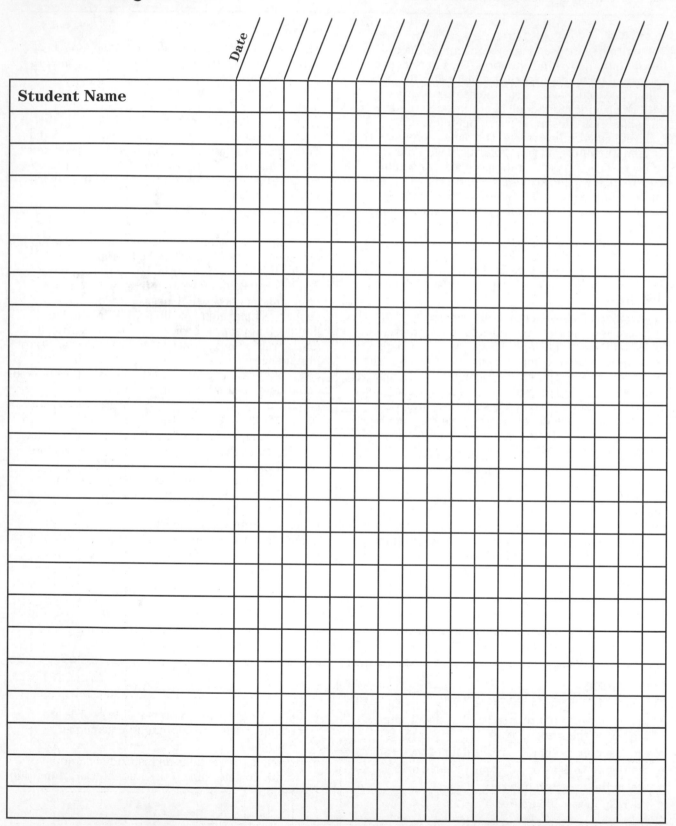

Student Name	Date																

Oral Fluency Scores

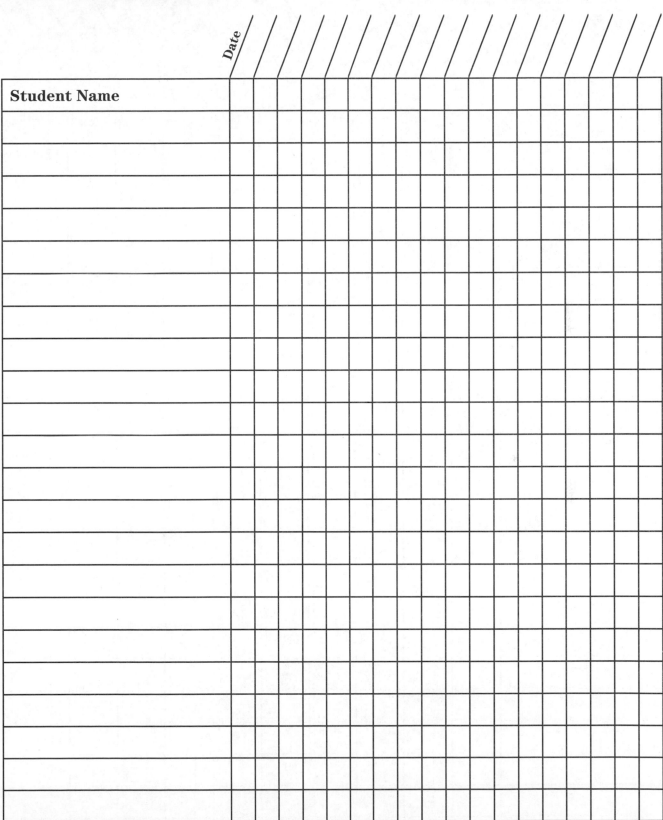

Student Name	Date														

Class Assessment Record

Student Name	Unit 4, Lesson 1	Unit 4, Lesson 2	Unit 4, Lesson 3	Unit 4, Lesson 4	Unit 4, Lesson 5	Unit 4 Writing Prompt	Unit 5, Lesson 1	Unit 5, Lesson 2	Unit 5, Lesson 3

Class Assessment Record

Student Name	Unit 5, Lesson 4	Unit 5, Lesson 5	Unit 5 Writing Prompt	Unit 6, Lesson 1	Unit 6, Lesson 2	Unit 6, Lesson 3	Unit 6, Lesson 4	Unit 6, Lesson 5	Unit 6 Writing Prompt

Lesson Assessment Book 2

Student Assessment Record

Name _____

Teacher _____ Grade _____

Unit/ Lesson	Assessment Section	Date	Number Possible	Number Right	%	Score (Rubrics/WPM)

Comprehension Observation Log

Student _____ **Date** _____

Unit _____ **Lesson** _____ **Selection Title** _____

General Comprehension
Concepts discussed: _____

_____

Behavior Within a Group
Articulates, expresses ideas: _____

_____

Joins discussions: _____

_____

Collaborates (such as *works well with other students, works alone*): _____

_____

Role in Group
Role (such as *leader, summarizer, questioner, critic, observer, non-participant*): _____

_____

Flexibility (changes roles when necessary): _____

_____

Use of Reading Strategies
Uses strategies when needed (either those taught or student's choice of strategy)/Describes strategies used:

_____

_____

_____

Changes strategies when appropriate: _____

_____

Changes Since Last Observation

_____

_____

_____
